W9-ASO-294

JAN 20 '85

MY UNIVERSE AND MY FAITH

MY UNIVERSE
and MY FAITH

A CATHOLIC LAYMAN'S VIEWS
ON SCIENCE AND HIS RELIGION

by

JOHN M. SPILMAN

EXPOSITION PRESS   NEW YORK

Ad majorem Dei gloriam

Exposition Press Inc., 386 Fourth Avenue, New York 16, N. Y.

FIRST EDITION

Preface

As THE EARTH REVOLVES AROUND, that is, before the sun, having its day and night, so have controversies been recurring with the exponents of Light and the exponents of Darkness, before God.

The topics discussed in this book have arisen continuously during the past centuries. The forces of Darkness have, and are now, striving for predominance in this world, with false ideologies and illusive fables, against the efforts of the forces of Light.

For almost fifty years, preparation, studies, and researches were made by me in the subjects contained in this book, with a work of many volumes in mind; but circumstances not being favorable and as people do not seem to be interested in a many-volume work, I have attempted, here, to condense everything into this one book. I have avoided exhaustive expressions of ideas and explanations, and endeavor to use as much plain language as possible.

This collective product is the result of my many years of accumulated study and investigation, and not the opinion of any church or religion. It is intended for people living in the Shadows of the Night, and especially for Roman Catholics.

The following chapters discuss matters of a scientific and religious nature; matters that are present about us and which should be seriously and attentively viewed.

To the numerous authors, scientists, and writers, living or dead, whose works I have perused during the years and from whom I have possibly derived some ideas, I wish to express my thanks and deep gratitude for the privilege of examining, and possibly using some of their ideas or opinions.

The reader should ponder every word and paragraph; it will help him to get out of the Darkness into the Light!

J. M. S.

Contents

The Prophet *that hath a Dream, let him tell a Dream; and he that hath* My *word, let him speak* My *word with* truth; *what hath the chaff to do with the wheat, saith the* LORD.   JEREMIAS 23:28

How long shalt this be in the heart of the Prophets *that prophesy lies, and that prophesy the delusions of their own heart? Who seek to make* My people *forget* My *Name through their* dreams, *which they tell every man to his neighbors; as their fathers forgot* My *Name for Baal.*
                                                              JEREMIAS 23:26-27

Am I, think ye, a God *at hand, saith the* LORD, *and not a* God, *afar off? Shall a man be hid in secret places and I not see him, saith the* LORD? *Do not I fill Heaven and Earth, saith the* LORD?   JEREMIAS 23:23-24

Atheists

Woe to the pastors, that destroy and tear the sheep of my pastures, saith the Lord.

JEREMIAS 23:1

WHEN A STUDENT ENTERS a non-religious school to study some form of science, it happens, in many instances, that his teachers are atheists, and their first effort is to destroy the new scholar's belief in God and religion. These teachers assume an attitude of authority in their subjects. By ridicule, they hope to make the learner forsake his acquired beliefs. They demand that he study in the spirit, discipline, and tradition of atheistic science, and then, by building up his pride and self-conceit, they believe they can accomplish their end. In comparison, this brings up a question: Must a person taking up the study of genealogy forsake his parents and family and later accept them if, by actual proof but not by word of mouth, they have proven that they are his parents and relatives? Such is their comparable demand.

Hence, the student absorbs atheistic opinions and ideas, drops his religion, and believes in nothing unless it is "proven" to him. He goes through life, like his professors, in a miserable rut of unbelief; will not lay aside his studies in matter for a moment to let a ray of sanity penetrate his brain, to investigate thoroughly the world of the spirit which he ignores. God and soul, he demands, must be set before him on a platter.

He becomes as one who would enter a large mansion, analyze all the materials of which it was built; take dimensions of the building and of its rooms; study the use and purpose of everything therein; and then inform you that everything there just happened by itself, and that no man built the house or made the furnishings and furniture. And, in addition, he would declare that there is no such thing as man.

Such are the usual beginnings of many of our atheistic scientists. They generate atheism, and the sophisticates learn from them, adopt their ideas, and live a life detrimental to their own souls and those of others.

The atheist does not believe in anything if it cannot be felt, seen, heard, tested, or counted. He thinks that to be real, everything must be based on his reason; on the knowledge of his kind; and on his scientific findings. He is like a man born blind, who would prefer to believe that there is no such thing as light or color which other men see. He contends that faith is contrary to his reason. Science is his God, and research his passion.

He does not consider a man as a psychic unit or a being tending toward God; only as a structural unit and a social entity. The spiritual phenomena, appearing in this world, in many forms, he ignores, because they cannot be proven to him materialistically. To him, everything must be within the bounds of matter, otherwise it is superstition and does not exist.

Even when a person chooses not to believe in any Spiritual or Supernatural Being, he realizes that if God, religion, and morality were eliminated, chaos and crime would dominate the world. Existence would be uncertain. Morality cannot exist without religion, or the latter without God. Even running a nation with an armed force and an iron fist, and enslaving the people, as is being done under Communism, will sooner or later break down into catastrophe. An atheistic world could not be a Paradise; it would resemble the Wild West of times gone by in the United States. You would have to carry a gun to survive, because you would not know what your friend or neighbor might be plotting against your life or property. There would be no moral restrictions to evil. Anarchy would prevail.

There are foods so refined that they give no nourishment; there are atheistic claims so refined that they are utterly senseless and valueless for the mind's good. Some assert that there must be a predisposition or a constant thought that works for a particular end, and then that end develops into being. If so, how come that before there was a brain, or sight, or hearing, such a thought could exist and know what end it was tending to? How did it know there could be such a thing as a brain or an eye or ear? Where was this "all-knowing, all-planning" sensitive center, or entity, which registered this thought or condition, thus giving it the power to come into materialistic being? Where did it get its intelligence and knowledge?

Some think that real things subsist without a mind, that they have a natural subsistence of their own. But this is an erroneous thought, because they follow the laws of Nature, and Nature is nothing else but Providence, which, in turn, is the art whereby God makes and governs everything; hence, they subsist on the Mind of God.

An atheist proclaims, "There is no God," from his heart and not from his head. Reason would tell him that he is mistaken. He has come to this frame of mind either through excess of pride or passion, never through the use of reason.

Emile Zola, for example, an archatheist, was so stubborn that when a miracle occurred in his presence at Lourdes, France, he covered his eyes and turned away, not wanting to see or believe.

A wise man would never make such a final statement as "There is no God." The various changes that have occurred in science in recent years show that one does not know what may be beyond the next scientific step. Being an Emile Zola, you will come to disbelieve yourself; you will go groping through your days; your way of life will not impart any meaning to your existence; you will come to the brink of despair and possible annihilation.

Final negative decisions as to the state of the future life, or God, or soul, should never be given. It has been proven, time and again, that what the atheist believes has not been right. At one time he based his convictions on the atom. The atom was smashed, and he was disillusioned. The age of the world was changed several times to his chagrin; evolution has not been proven a fact; it is still a theory based on circumstantial evidence.

Materialistic ideas were created, because the materialists could not measure religious or mystical matters, all metaphysical principles and occult laws, by the three dimensions—length, breadth, and thickness. Since when have these dimensions become universal in use? Has anyone measured the properties of the elements by them? Or the substance of gas? Or the atoms, or electrons, protons, and neutrons by them? No! No one ever did! The atheist asserts that these dimensions were used to measure time and space. How? They may measure space but not time. Time really measures them!

Thought is like a seed. The religious man lives according to rule, and his thought-seed is planted, fertilized, cultivated, and attended to. It brings him ultimate benefit! The unbeliever, not wishing to live by the rule of God and religion, has his brains overrun with weeds, bringing him ultimate loss!

Apostles of Atheism

Now, A CONVINCED ATHEIST is a rare article. Most of these who claim to be atheistic are really agnostics or skeptics. Most of today's bigotry and prejudice against God and religion has been acquired from the atheistic philosophers and writers of the more recent centuries.

In those days of the beginning of social science, many writers became atheistic or agnostic, because they did not know how complicated a thing this physical and social universe really was. Their loss of faith was shallow and silly; they were paragons of narrow-mindedness and superficial thinking. They were lost in a world of human progress. God could not teach anything to most of these people; they knew everything.

As all during the history of the Church, there were many evil writers and attackers who concentrated upon fighting her dogmas; the more recent enemies take it upon themselves to destroy God, religion, and the Church. With the various scientific discoveries and evolutionary theories arising, and with the basing of their learning upon the atom, many of these so-called learned men think they are so advanced that they are beyond the Supreme Being and do not have any use for God and religion. "Science disproves God, science disproves religion," is their silly proclamation.

But this statement is not coming from all scientists. The majority of them know better. They refute that old cry and give testimony that there must be and is a God, and that there must be a religion. It is the intellectuals, those of scant religious learning or wrong training, and the Communists who propagate the old absurdities under the name of science.

Hysteria and degeneration were rampant in previous centuries. The multitude of discoveries and innovations that came suddenly upon the mentally fatigued God-haters provided favorable conditions for them. They could seek escape and spread their sickness to endanger our spiritual world. Many of them suffered from a fixation—hatred of authority. They took it out on God, religion, and the Church. Their writings were used to find an excuse, or provide evidence, for their mode of living or position in life. If some of those apostles of atheism lived today, psychiatry would have revealed that they labored under a mental disturbance; that they were mentally unbalanced.

It is well known that a degenerate can be a genius. He can attain a high degree of intellectual power, although, from the moral point of view, his existence is completely deranged. And many of those people were gifted degenerates. Take away from them the special faculties that made them geniuses, and there would remain only a criminal or a madman. Hatred of authority and a fixed idea of persecution developed the mentality of most of them. Readers of their works who delight in or admire their opinions must suffer, as a rule, from hysteria, neurosis, or various complexes.

Causation of disease by germs, gravity, radiation, electronics, were not known well, if at all, in their time. Their writings and beliefs were based upon a small and undeveloped field of research. In their world, learned and prominent persons believed in witches and had people murdered for witchery. Philosophies written in such an era of degeneration are hardly worthwhile reading. "Modern thinkers" assume the attitude of independent and impartial observers. No one can be independent or impartial. Each of us begins with a bias that is temperamental, educative, and circumstantial. We may change or modify our views, but we never leave the place from which we view the universe. These "thinkers" work with minds full of suspicion, mistrust, and dislike. Their whole current of opinion is and has been hostile to religion and especially to the Church of Rome. Their basic learning is derived from the works of the limited mentalities of previous centuries.

It behooves us to be careful and use the common sense with which God has endowed our intelligence, in all of our reasoning, perusals, investigations, etc., and to try to differentiate between bias and impartiality; to know authority when present or when missing; to try to discover an obscurantist, when one seems not clear or when a truth appears to be hidden; to weigh all argument in the light of the Church's teachings, before we accept or acknowledge it as genuine, and before we believe any speaker or writer about whom we know little or nothing. Let us beware of any and all evil scientists, philosophers, persons with degrees, and false authorities.

Passions blind not only the savage, but also the learned, so that they do not see the light which seeks to enlighten them.

Atheism

Take care, therefore, that the light that is in thee is not darkness.

LUKE 11:35

ATHEISM, IN MOST INSTANCES, is the direct culmination of a philosophy of life constructed to justify wrong conduct. People choose the modes of life they wish to follow, and build a philosophy about it to justify their manner of living, instead of first constructing their philosophy and then patterning their lives accordingly. Their minds are clouded with doubts concerning God, not because of what they think, but because of the kind of lives they lead. This was prevalent in past centuries, and holds true with many individuals living today.

Previous to the smashing of the atom, there were some confirmed atheistic scientists who believed they had the solution to the riddle of the world. They developed such pride in their discoveries that they proposed to reduce all conduct and morals to a set of chemical and mathematical equations. Their conceited belief did not materialize, because they found that atoms were not the ultimate particles. They found that the more you know, the more you have to learn.

The most outstanding founders of modern science always possessed faith in the Almighty God. They recognized that the law and order in this universe required an Intelligent Cause. They looked at Darwin's evolution and considered it an absurdity. They could not understand how an aggregation of blind causes could produce the universe and the intelligent beings within it. Nor how any combination of molecules, left to chance or hazard, could bring about an order similar to that found in living organisms, where not only are union, cohesion, and combination, but also a principle of life and action, and also intelligence and moral order. They could not believe evolution was the expression of a purposive dynamic force which could create living organisms, and that it could be capable of processing its own development, because they would have been granting it the status of a god, and endowing it with a supernatural intelligence. They knew that no one thing in Nature was the cause of Nature's order. They knew that this order in Nature implies that there can never be any blind chances in evolution, because no positive thing can come of nothing. They knew that the universe is an orderly and dependable place, with regularities among the complex events of Nature. These events do not occur at random, but follow definite laws. That order suggests purpose. Purpose suggests a mind. And this mind suggests no one but God.

It is pitiable that certain persons have such an inclination to listen readily to the wrong scientists, when these express their prejudicial opinions concerning God and religion. They know that each one of these bigoted learned men is only a master in his particular field, and that it does not follow that each is an authority in art, music, philosophy, or theology. In matters that are religious and spiritual, each one is actually, you might say, illiterate, because he has given far less study to these things.

Why should it be assumed that any bigoted scientist is either a philosopher or a theologian because he understands mathematics or chemistry, any more than it should be assumed that the philosopher or theologian should be highly rated as a doctor or artist? Why do certain people give weight to a scientist's opinions in matters of God and religion, and disregard a person who has spent his life studying his God and His works? Why should anyone refer to such a meddler as an authority in the spiritual light, when, as a scientist, he does not concern himself with the origin of things, but only with their composition and with the laws that govern them, when the study of causes is not the province of science, but of metaphysics? Prejudice and ignorance provide the reason.

When an unbeliever bases his faith in no God, religion, or Church, because he has taken the words of some atheist, he professes a gross stupidity. His efforts to visualize God reveal a surprising childishness. We can no more conceive Him than we can conceive an electron. This incapacity to visualize is not, in itself, a proof of non-existence. One cannot visualize an electron, proton, or neutron, but still firmly believes in them. Their existence is not doubted for an instant.

Our entire organized, living universe becomes incomprehensible without the hypothesis of God. Not to believe in Him, but to believe in some physical elements of which one knows very little, is an irrational faith. Many persons are not aware of it!

Though we cannot conceive God, we can and do conceive the idea of God, and the fact that we can conceive the idea of God is in itself a unique proof that God exists.

All Nature is a book, on every page of which we can read of the Almighty. When we look up to the heavens and then consider the laws which govern the heavenly bodies, we are amazed at His wisdom. We are equally amazed when, under the microscope, we examine the tiniest insects; when we consider the instincts of all animals, birds, and bees. We know laws do not make themselves. They imply a lawgiver. We know there is a God, and we do not need to prove His existence when He is so obvious.

"Cultured Intelligentsia"

SOME PERSONS, often with an uncompleted education, after spending a few years in reading and memorizing the contents of books on serious topics, or having taken a college course for some degree, become obsessed with their own superiority. Having spent their time reading controversial material or studying under teachers who have no faith in God or religion, they consider themselves on a higher strata of culture than the common man.

These people move about in circles of their own kind; live their lives in a sophisticated atmosphere, and are always ready to adopt ideas that are of, or are for, the benefit of some atheistic or crackpot clique.

They live on the mountaintops and look down upon the valley. The people in the valley appear to them to be laden down with superstition and ignorance. Their hearts break because they find these people will not listen to them. The valley people contend that only he who lives in the valley, among them, can understand and work out their problems, and not one whose eyes glow with prejudice and who lives in exaltation.

The people of the valley believe in God and have religion, and know that the principles of common sense are the common inheritance of every intellect and serve to help man in all of his reasoning, decisions, and daily duties, while these "cultured intelligentsia" have no common sense but live with a fixation of ideas, or a lost-sheep mentality.

The valley people are not entirely wrong in their estimations. When one lives among the introverts, he notices that they live an empty life, grasping here and there for reading matter which seems to them highly cultural, to fill in their time. Anything that has prejudice, or is biased, against any prevailing religion, is top goods. Things written with a religious flavor or for religion are passé. Those whose minds are as of lost sheep, though having no regard for established religion, will nevertheless interest themselves in the glamor of mysticism and occultism.

During the present time the "C.I.'s" get themselves into good government positions, and there use their biased influence to the detriment of the nation's safety; to the irritation of the churches and their members; and for the good of obnoxious foreign agencies.

In matters of God, soul, and religion, these persons are skeptics, not because of their intellects, but because of their mode of living, educational training, and moral behavior. They do not really want the truth, they wish to be confirmed in their opinions. They assume an attitude of independence in their thinking and hate to have their ideas modified. Anything that would attract their attention to religious subjects they avoid like the plague. Their prejudices are the products of their mental and emotional make-up: If cornered into a discussion of a religious subject, they squirm or will argue you senseless, hating to admit you are right, even if you are.

They contend that evil people go to church and should be compelled to live right. They hate coercion in matters of their personal thoughts and behavior, but for someone else it is passable.

Few of the "C.I.'s" are creative. There are a few who will search and have faith in their findings until proved wrong, but they are very few. The majority are imitators; they adopt their false ideas from other sources and cling to them, resisting all efforts to be righted. They live in imitation because it is an escape from reality and the truth. Their weakness of soul is their strength.

Now, all of these sophisticates are not college-bred people, although some are, but the vast number have various degrees of education. It is the spirit of antagonism against God and religion that spurs them to read and study the wrong books. It satisfies their egos. It gives them a feeling of revenge and satisfaction, because they are resigned to their fate. Because they are like all who live without a final spiritual aim or end, their life is haphazard. They have no definite port to sail to, no direct course affixed to a star of salvation. As they have no proper and good spiritual object to aim at in their earthly sojourn, they are less careful to guide themselves toward a heavenly goal.

Few men are so evil as not to have some rational moments. When in such moments, cannot they show some pity on their own souls? Show some mercy to themselves? Must they be enemies of God and fugitives from their own consciences? Do not ridicule man, think! Stop and think! You cannot sail the sea of life like a ship without a spiritual rudder. You are destined to be dashed to pieces against the rocks and reefs of life and circumstances. Remember the story of the Prodigal in the Bible? Read and consider it!

Written Prejudice and Its Authors

MANY A BOOK HAS BEEN WRITTEN or edited, composed of many controversial subjects concerning philosophy, religion, and evolution, and the authors or compilers of said book or books would state that the writings are unbiased and unprejudicial to anyone; but, on thorough examination, it would be revealed that a subtle foundation of partiality toward bias exists therein. A bias directed mainly against God, religion, or Church.

Why was it written so? Why, to pretend fairness, and, in the meanwhile, poison the mind of the unsuspecting reader, knowing that, though people may have an education, the great percentage of them lack a sense of responsibility; they do not think for themselves.

The author or compiler would say that, though there are some strong articles against God, religion, or the Church, there are also a few articles in their favor. These, he claims, show him as impartial. But just wander through the book and count them all! Yes, you will find that the number of biased articles greatly outnumber those that are in favor, and that is called impartiality! Besides, the articles written in favor would be of such weak structure, concerning themselves mostly with irrelevant matters, or be in a condensed form, so as to be of little or no value.

The atheistic writers try to explain God, religion, or the Church, but, not being members of a church or religion, how can they understand? It is not the outsider who can give you the correct picture of any organization, but the one who is in the midst of its activities. One who is inside and faithful to his organization understands his position; and his faith and everything connected with it.

From their infancy most of the biased writers breathed an air hostile to God and religion; they have spent their lives moving in a current of opinion which has been antagonistic to the tenets of faith; and their minds were always full of dislike, suspicion, and distrust. Some suffered from a fixation or some form of insanity; others wrote wholly to find an excuse for their mode of living. They could not be convinced that they could be wrong, because the eyes of prejudice are never open to facts, no matter how recent.

Most of the anti-religious works were composed and published during the period from the sixteenth to the nineteenth century. Many people living in this age, when knowledge has advanced so much as to make those works obsolete and unsuited to our times, still refer to, or study them, and bring forth outdated arguments against God and religion, little realizing that those philosophies need consignment to the garbage can.

Have you ever evaluated the standards of education these materialists possessed? No? Why, a high-school student of today receives, and has, a higher standard of learning, with more advanced knowledge of things than they ever possessed. In their day much of science was not known; they were groping in the dark; their beginning and end was the atom, and on this they based their wrong theories. Some persons persisted, even to the twentieth century, to foster their wrong notions in spite of advanced scientific knowledge.

How can anyone today be so condescending as to give credence to these biased writers whose reasoning was based on inferior standards of education and experience? Many of them were psychiatrically deficient, as Nietzsche, who did his best work when he had a pain in the head; or Thomas Paine, who was not sure if the world revolved or was at rest? If our "modernists" employ such biased ravings as a basis of their education, can one be surprised at the low level of their intelligence in matters of life and spirit?

Authority

IN DISCUSSIONS, some people present facts by backing them up with an authority. This authority usually happens to be someone famous in something irrelevant to the matter under discussion. Approval should not be given on a debated point, if the person cited is not an authority on the subject discussed. It may be only that person's personal opinion which is quoted. It behooves us not to take the word of a bricklayer upon the work of a carpenter; or the word of an electrician upon the labors of a medical man; or the conviction of a famous person upon a subject of which he has made no thorough study. Much biased literature is supported with such erroneous authorities.

A person who has studied a topic perfectly and completely as possible can be acknowledged to be an accepted source of information on the matter, but that does not give him equal mastery over other subjects of which he has only a slight, or a synoptic, acquaintance. A synopsis of a thing is helpful in understanding it, but a synoptic mind does not make one an authority.

No one in this world can be an all-around authority on every topic that arises. If there be one, he would have to possess a complete universal mind. By universal mind, I mean he would have to have a complete and thorough knowledge of everything in this vast universe, from the infinitesimal parts of an electron to the last distant star. He would have to know all the languages spoken or written; all that exist and have existed. He would have to know all professions and trades; all spiritual as well as all materialistic matters. He would have to know everything there is to know!

No one ever lived or ever will live on this planet who can attain a universal mind, because our finite nature has limitations. We cannot grasp with our finite minds the things which only an infinite mind can comprehend. And there is only one mind which can have a complete and thorough knowledge of everything; where all is recorded to the last detail, and where nothing is lacking. That mind is the Mind of God! He, alone, has the Universal Mind! He knows everything there is to know; He is the only All-Complete Authority and the only Infinite Mind!

A prevailing superstition exists that a person who has a string of degrees following his name is an authority on almost everything. This is absurd! One who studies a subject and gives his time to learn it can only discuss that subject properly with someone who also understands it. Because they who have their substance know more about it than any who have not!

Persons who are most able in one field are liable to be deficient in another. Men whom we regard as "brilliant" are not necessarily brilliant in every respect. The total personality of an individual comprises many different items. It is the sum total of all the characteristics and training which make up a distinctive individual. We cannot classify any as brainy, brainier, and brainiest, because there are so many different qualities of mind and personal ability. The more degrees a person has, the more his world of knowledge is enlarged, but still he may stay deficient in many ways, and not really "know all."

To use the opinion of a learned person as an authoritative statement, where the knowledge expected is limited or wanting, is to accept a false premise; you cannot bring forth something important from lack of knowledge and experience. Common sense insists that one never finds something coming from nothing. If the know-how is not there, it cannot give birth to itself in that learned person's mind. Opinions expressed we must accept as opinions and not as authoritative statements, unless we know positively the background of the person expressing the opinion. Our enemies find that they can convince us in an argument concerning God, religion, or Church by mentioning some important intellectual as the authority for their assertions, trusting that our ignorance, at that moment, will accept him and the statement credited to him.

Expressions of opinion by some learned on things outside their immediate fields of endeavor may involve value judgments that are entirely foreign to the thing considered. A certain caution is required. A man should remain within his own proper field of inquiry, to avoid the possibility of introducing value judgments where they may be irrelevant and even harmful.

About Research

In contemplation of created things,
By steps we may ascend to God.
                                                            MILTON

GOD DOES NOT SHOW HIMSELF directly to us as in a mirror. To see God's reflection in His works, man must be attentive to them. One cannot see God, because this universe is composed of the seen and the unseen. As atoms, electronic particles, cosmic rays, etc., which belong to the unseen, so does God. As the unseen can only be revealed by experiment, mathematics, research, investigation, and such, so does God have to be revealed to the unbeliever by various methods of research. When the research is in material things, it is called science; when it is in immaterial things, it belongs to metaphysics, a part of philosophy. When science goes probing God or the soul, which are spirit and not matter, it goes out of its province; it is thereby invading the field of theology and so ceases to be science. This science which is so admirably adapted to show forth the glory of God, the Great Creator, is regrettably, perversely promulgated.

Though we know science is a limited study, people also have a habit of classing other studies under that heading, whether they are related or not.

Research came about because man can concentrate, reason, and get ideas. Animals cannot, because their minds are limited. Research did not come in a haphazard way as atheistic evolution surmises matter and life did. Conception of an idea or notion requires more than one fact. One fact is not knowledge, it is hardly perceptible. When one fact is compared with another; when inferences are drawn that are considered in relation to other facts, then an idea is born; then research and science are in the making. This science is knowledge correctly classified with respect to interrelated facts; this science tells us the "how" of things, where religion tells us the "why."

If the universe were not an orderly and dependable place, science could not exist. Being an orderly procedure, science concerns itself with finding the underlying laws and regularities that exist in the complex events of its nature. All of these events prove they do not occur at random, but follow definite laws, and the scientist endeavors to find these laws. It is the orderliness of the universe that gives the scientist his faith, because of its dependability, to make his search. Order suggests purpose. To have purpose, the end of every law—it is hard to imagine how it could have been created and is operated without there being a mind behind it.

When we study natural history we find it a history of the work of God, and no demonstration of His existence is more within the understanding of all than that which Nature's own story affords us. And in this story of the earth, which reveals definite signs of God's plans, geology holds very many records.

In our physical world, modern mathematicians find numerous applications which show that everything here is done with number, weight, and measure. This gives them great admiration for the disposing and ordering Cause in the world, who is God. Also, by the unwavering mathematical law, they can prove that our universe was designed and executed by a great engineering Intelligence, which, again, is God.

Of the magnificent law and order of Nature, God is the personification. The marvelous and implacable orderliness which research reveals is the manifestation of the Almighty, the work of the Creator. We can grasp Him from the point of view of truth, of law and order of Nature. Who refuses to believe in that denies his faith in the power and permanence of God; he becomes similar to the atheists, who were and are a product of the Reformation's aftermath. The Divine Existence is far more evidently perceived than the existence of man, because the effects of Nature are infinitely more numerous and considerable than those ascribed to human agents.

Science, itself, is not atheistic, it does not proclaim, "There is no God." It is merely the voicing of a certain portion of those who deal in it. As a rotten apple in a barrel will spoil the rest, so it happens that a product of the Reformation's consequences has spent his poison among those who came to study under him, and those, in turn, passed on the poison to others, and these to others, and so on up to the present time. The rotten apple may smear the barrel with its rottenness, but the barrel has nothing to do with it. The barrel does not claim it came of nothing and that it has no owner; it knows it is here only to serve.

Research has not only proven facts, but it has established theories. Theories are ideas that have not been proven. Many of them are fallacies. To accept them as facts, as some people do, is erroneous. Evolutionary theories, taken for an instance, are still unproven circumstantial guesses; and many of our physical laws are merely statistical or partly theorized statements. These statements hold good for the average of a great number of cases. They have no meaning for an individual case, because the laws of physical processes are limited. And research, without even a theory, reveals that Nature, itself, is not homogeneous and that there is a solution of continuity between inorganic matter and life which science cannot account for. As to the ultimate constituents of matter and of their natures, science has no facts or theories.

Hence, research benefits us and increases our understanding in one way, and in another it can do harm and make trouble when its theories are misinterpreted. Natural science shows forth the glory of the Great Creator, and, in spite of the theories, it should be taught with that in mind.

The Unseen Realm

THE WORLD DOES NOT EXIST for itself or from itself; it could not give birth to itself. Behind the physical world is another, more fundamental realm, which cannot be described in physical terms. In this non-physical realm lies the ultimate origin of all things, of life and of consciousness; of energy, matter, and organization.

Our consciousness is rooted in a world not built of atoms; and the human mind, in its facets, reflects some of the fundamental characteristics of its origin, God. Thinking and planning are important characteristics of our minds, and they must have their origin in a realm beyond our physical selves. You cannot conceive of thinking and planning without a personality that does the work. In the universe it is the World Soul, or God, as we know Him.

The phenomena in this world are physical and non-physical. The vibrations of a musical instrument are physical, but our sensations of sound and music belong to the non-physical. The rays of the sun have physical properties, but our sensations of light and color are non-physical. Energy (matter is considered as energy also) emerges from a non-physical state, as photons and corpuscles, into a physical domain. This energy fills the whole universe; and the celestial space, sometimes referred to as a "void," is shot through and through with radiant energy.

When we bombard molecules and produce changes, we do not destroy or create anything from nothing. There, in the vast unseen realm, are agents, properties, and powers of which the scientist has learned little, wherein the seemingly destroyed things find location and apparent new matter appears, its formation made possible by means of the influence of the properties of the bombardment, or by means of the bombarding medium and other unseen agents or properties.

Limited evolution can be behind the changing of forms of matter, but only a Supreme Intelligence, existing in the unseen universe, can be behind that evolution. Only this Great Mind can direct the placing of a shell around an egg, or the works of the various roots of the various plants in their power to select differing materials from the selfsame soil.

Motion did not produce itself; in space where there are few or no anti-motional forces, a rotation once started can keep on and on; on the earth where there is gravity, atmosphere, friction of all kinds, motion cannot be continuous without there being a force present to propel it. At the birth of the universe, motion was not automatically born of itself, there was an outside Cause, existing in the unseen world, that produced that motion; a Cause having will and intelligence. This Cause produced the force which gave the initial impulse that brought the universe into being and its worlds in whirls, both in the visible and invisible realms. This power must have existed before the universe was created, and it did not disappear with that first impulse, but has continued throughout the ages.

This First Cause is a Spirit, because intelligence is a faculty proper to simple spiritual substances. It is distinct from the visible world, which is formed of various composed corporeal substances. That Spirit, whose life is intellectual, knows and wills—in a word, it is a Personal God. This is what the order of Nature reveals to us, and the argument drawn from the world's harmony suffices to refute the many fundamental errors existing today.

Behind the visible material universe, the unseen realm lies inaccessible to our intellect and our physical senses. In this realm, open to the insight of the spirit, we find the source of beauty, goodness, and love. Here, too, one feels the presence of some-thing vastly greater than ourselves, a Spirit to whom, in some mysterious way, we are related and upon whom we are depend-ent. Our constructive capacity to understand this Spirit, whom we call God, does not go beyond the world of the artificial. We cannot measure Him by earthly measurements. We cannot prove Him like a mathematical equation. We are limited to the bound-aries of our own vision and senses. We cannot ever embrace the horizons of God through our limited capacities. We cannot trust the eye or ear. We only can trust in the Omniscient God.

Every organism is made up of two parts, one visible and one invisible; the invisible being of greater importance. Man, being an organism, has a visible body and an invisible soul. From this soul he gets life, and from it all his vital actions pro-ceed. This soul was endowed with an innate intelligence; it was not created or developed by man. He was endowed with it by the Universal Intelligence, of which it is a part, and he has simply acquired the capacity of making use of it.

As sound is graded on a piano, or the elements in chemistry, things in the seen and unseen realms are graded. The organiza-tion of animal bodies is produced in this gradation order from which the idea of evolution was born. We also have a gradation of man and the spirit world in the following form: Life with body and without soul—Cell; life with body and soul—Man; life with soul without body—Angels; and all life and all soul, unlimited—God. God being the highest in the spiritual world; man, between spirit and matter.

The visible and invisible universe contains signs which show plainly that it was the work of an intelligent Being. These signs display a high degree of wisdom united to immense power; this intelligence does not reside in the things themselves, and, there-fore, the world was created and is governed by that intelligent Being, whom we call God.

The Universe and Existing Opposites

THE SPACE THROUGH WHICH this planet twirls is not a simple void or vacuum, but is filled with a thin gas, representing the outer reaches of the sun's atmosphere; and with radiant energy. This extremely thin gas is a hundred times denser than expected. The space is peppered with dust from comets which are going to pieces. There are cosmic rays which are not as much of a hazard as the radiation danger which is one thousand times greater than that from the cosmic rays. It comes from the electrified particles shot out from the sun, which envelop the earth. The cosmic rays are fast-moving particles, the others are slow-moving. When they hit an object, they produce intense X rays within that object, and are deadlier than the cosmic rays.

The earth's atmosphere extends upward to possibly 30,000 miles, instead of 180 to 250 miles, as was formerly believed. Out in space there are no north, south, east, or west. There are no top, bottom, or sides; only that which may be evident from the presence of gravity.

The universe at its origin was composed only of inanimate molecular matter. It was also believed that at that period the sun and stars were formed of the same percentage of chemical elements as those which have been studied on our earth. This assumption has been found erroneous and has been abandoned.

During the early history of our globe, the earth was flat and featureless, with many areas completely covered by shallow seas. It is only a comparatively short time since the mountains were raised. As there was much destructive rain in the early eras, floods could have been present anywhere. And as life would have flown for safety to any nearby mountain, such a one could not have been very high, because it, as all the other mountains, was being washed into the sea. Denials of floods existing in the earlier era have no factual basis.

The universe, which is billions of years old, is not an idea, and you are not in a dream world, as it was contended by an insane philosopher of a recent century. You are a reality and, no matter what your body or the universe is made up of, the world is a reality to you. You are not a delusion because you exist and are conscious of yourself. Though your body changes completely every seven years, and your brain every day, you are still a being living in a real world. In your existence there is the "now" or present moment of which you are conscious. This moment reveals to you that you exist and are laboring in some way, either mentally or physically, upon or within some existing premise, the world. And the representation or depiction of this external world, or existence, in the seat of your consciousness, in the brain, is evidence of your reality.

Are there any perfections in the universe? you may ask. Yes, there are many perfections in the universe, but none of them is sufficient to produce itself. Therefore, they are all derived from a Being who possesses all of them in an eminent and causative manner. That Perfect Being is God.

Modern science tells us that the amount of entropy, or unavailable energy, is constantly on the increase in this universe. When all of the world's energy will have passed out under this form, the temperatures of the universe will be uniform; all activity will cease, and the world will come to an end. Had our world existed from eternity, complete entropy would have been reached ages upon ages ago, and this universe would have been finished. This is evidence that our world was created and that God keeps it under His Divine care.

"All things are double, one against another, and he hath made nothing defective" (Eccles. 42:25).

In Nature, everything depends upon action and reaction; the whole universe is held together by mutual attraction and repulsion. These two great forces contend against each other. They are called the centrifugal—or inside—and the centripetal—or outside—forces. All agents of change come of two kinds; one builds up and the other opposes, or tears down. The actions of volcanos and earthquakes help to build up mountains and valleys; the action of water, in its many forms as rain, rivers, tides, frost, snow, etc., tends to tear or wear down and level; application of heat will warm up a thing; application of ice will cool it; friction from outside sources will burn or bruise a limb; forces from inside the limb will try to restore it to normal; there are expansion and contraction, and many other sets of opposites.

Everywhere we are confronted with opposites to everything that we may be concerned with on this earth, outside of the absolute. We have, also, the positive and the negative, life and death, health and disease, good and evil, light and darkness, peace and war, day and night, etc. As soon as a force ceases to progress, an opposite force dominates, and this force may cause the former one to recede to a point of equilibrium, inertia, or normalcy. To produce in evolution, a thought, desire, or condition would have to be constant, uninterrupted, because as soon as any lapse or pause occurs, the opposite tendency works to restore the situation to its former normal state. Materialists overlook many of these opposites in their consideration of things in this universe. In many ways, these contraries give the lie to their claims, especially where these opposing factors may make their presence probable. In one instance, they claim that at the formation of the first molecules of life there were no dangerous obstacles to their development, that only in later years did they become evident. This is not true. As there was law and order from the first day of creation, there were opposites present at the formation of life's cells. In some form or another they were there, and the molecules had to contend with them.

To mention more opposites, we have things that can be beautiful or ugly, useful or harmful, pleasant or painful, etc.; if there can be a patriot in a country, there can be a traitor; if there be a saint in a church, there can be a devil; and there are many more examples. In the unseen realm, our conscience reveals an inkling of what to expect in these contraries; there are pleasure and beauty as well as sorrow and pain, these providing indications of a Heaven and Hell.

Man, per se, is a duality consisting of a body and a spirit. The body is of matter, its spirit is the soul which animates it.

Man as a duality has control of his bodily and spiritual actions. He possesses inherent knowledge of what is decent and what is not, meaning he has realization.

Mankind is governed by pleasure and pain; they are the instruments with which man has to work and live. His happiness or misery is a matter of the objects of his loves or hates, be they natural or sensual. He, in comparison, must clear away weeds, bush, and trees so that he can raise food for his body; as he must remove all temptation and sin to gain salvation for his soul. Should he cease and lay away his tools for a short period, the weeds, bush, and trees will engulf and destroy him; so also should he discontinue his efforts against the works of the Devil; sin will overpower and damn him.

Atoms

THERE ARE ABOUT A HUNDRED different kinds of atoms, and these are built out of a number of fundamental particles. The laws governing the activities of these particles are relatively simple, and yet out of these laws is fashioned all of the richness of Nature. In the ramifications of their activities come into being the substances of which the universe is composed and the properties which govern their activities. It is because of the laws of these fundamental particles that we have light and mechanisms in our eyes to make use of it; the reality of the marvelous interrelation of organisms represented by our own bodies; the colorful beauty of flowers; the enticing scent that attracts the insects and furthers the purpose of fertilization.

Electrons, protons, neutrons, and the other particles form atoms; these are organized into molecules, some of the molecules into living cells, and some of the cells into increasingly complex animals, plants, and man. Sharing with other animals his physical characteristics, man nevertheless differs from all other creatures in certain important intellectual capacities, and in all, or nearly all, his spiritual attributes.

The inconceivably small atom is itself a system, and its constituents whirl in their orbits with incredible swiftness. No atom can be created or transformed other than in accordance with the dominating universal law.

The atom has a nucleus around which the electron revolves in an orbit, like a planet revolves about the sun. These tiny atomic solar systems are mainly space; the electrons and the nucleus take up only a minute fraction of that space. Since atoms make up molecules, and these, in turn, the larger masses of matter, the material universe must be mainly space, studded at intervals with an almost infinite number of infinitesimal electrical charges. For instance, we may take a rock for an example. When thinking deeply, a common man would think of it as a real piece of solid matter, but, to a scientist, the rock in fact would not be very real. It would be viewed as a shadowy swirling set of electric charges, these charges themselves being vague and elusive. For the scientist the rock would lose its illusion of solidity.

This space in the atom makes the atom porous. As we have a "void" in interstellar space, so we have a void in the atom, which was previously considered a solid and now is known to be only a mass of tiny specks floating in a void.

The universe is not considered today as it was before the splitting of the atom, and all of the traditional concepts of matter have been changed because of the discoveries made. The two fundamental laws of physics, the conservation of matter and the conservation of energy, were scrapped.

Combinations of atoms make a molecule. This material molecule is of itself inert and unconscious; but the materialist wants you to believe that, being without intelligence, it does intelligent work; being blind, it engenders harmony; though improvident, provides everything; though fortuitous, creates order, not only once but a thousand times repeated; though unconscious, knows how to construct with all the skill and ability of consummate science; which again, without soul, begets both life and soul; though without reason or sentiment, produces wonders of genius and love. How preposterous can such a person be? Why, in spite of his education, can he be so limited, so one-sided? How in common sense can he prove that these inert and unconscious molecules can of themselves unite together, dispose and arrange themselves in the precise order which an end demands? How can blind chance or hazard alone select and unite thousands, nay millions, of molecules into parts, and place these parts precisely where their properties will serve a special purpose and concur to an unique end?

The wonders of the construction of man, animal, plant, and of everything else in this universe, including their various parts, their compositions, forms, functions, etc., assuredly cannot be attributed to the fatal, blind evolution of primitive molecules. These organized beings or things present numerous characters of order and finality which absolutely require an intelligent Cause, which is God, who knows all things and directs all things, because He was and is the Architect and Creator of everything. These wonders all have order, and order also calls for an intelligent power back of it; because wherever we find parts, agents, or gadgets united and disposed in a regular manner, concurring as so many means to a common end, we are forced to recognize an intelligence, which knows, preconceives, desires, and adapts them to their end. The end would not be an end if it were not preconceived or desired. Nothing is produced in this universe without sufficient reason. God reflects Himself in everything, He shows Himself to man, but there are some men engrossed in prejudice who cannot see, who do not want to see.

Atheistic Evolution

I

EVOLUTION IS A SCIENTIFIC GENERALIZATION of change and always subject to change.

Quite often things are not as one assumes they are. In the history of science there were frequent differences between appearance and reality.

It is fantastic to believe that blind causes began this universe, because nothing reveals such a condition existed or was possible. It was manufactured to avoid an allusion to God, or the idea of a Supernatural Creator. This false assumption has built a "castle in the sky" for the atheist, as, in similar fashion, fiction writers build up a plot and compose a story about it.

From the time when the earth was a completely molten spheroid to the present era, it is calculated to be $4\frac{1}{2}$ billion years. If the moon was born out of the Pacific basin, it would be $1\frac{1}{2}$ billion years at a time when the earth's crust was hardening. The age of the earth's crust, measured by the radioactivity in rocks, is much the same as that of the dispersed galaxies of billions of stars, revealing all were created at the same time.

In the beginning, before creation, there was no chaos, as there was nothing existing. Soon after the start of creation, there may have been a state of happenings that appeared as chaos, but was not an actual chaotic state, it was simply an evolvement of things in a planned order, everything following its course and development according to certain laws, to the attainment of its next stage; and these kept on, in the same manner, evolving until the proper and more comprehensive grades were reached. Though the evolution set up by the First Cause, God, did not stop there, it has continued on as per His plans and directions.

The creative power of the Almighty working constantly in the evolutionary processes offers the only rational explanation of the universe and of the progressive march of life from the lowest to the highest forms. He created the first germinal forms of life and endowed them with potentialities to evolve into higher forms, according to definite laws He infused into them.

The order of Nature is a planned system, and everything developing had to proceed according to a planned system—and this was not born of itself, it was established here by a Great Intelligence. There was no sudden or spontaneous generation or other fixations. Proper scientists reject such notions whereby atheists build up their religion against religion. God created life and brought it out of the waters onto the land. He created all other living things on the earth, culminating in the making of man in His own image and likeness and endowing him with a soul, and He is still creating, as Jesus said, "My Father works even until now and I work" (John 5:17).

It is estimated that rocks were formed about $1\frac{1}{2}$ billion years ago. From the formation of the rocks to the present stage of the world, it appears that $1\frac{1}{2}$ billion years are undercalculated. If it took a few hundred million years for evolvement of a cell and then took almost that much to produce a sufficient amount of the cells to start their real work, almost a billion years would have been consumed in that way. Then it is assumed that it took a few hundred million years more for a supposed complex organic molecule to form; this would bring us up almost to our present era, which is not correct, because again this complex organic molecule would have taken many extra hundreds of millions of years to form the first living creature to crawl on this planet, and many, many more hundreds of millions of years to reach a stage where man would have been evident.

There being an assumed $1\frac{1}{2}$ or slightly more billions of years from the rock era, the many hundreds of millions of years of evolution would have extended far beyond that figure, or the figures used for the duration of each and all of the epochs. The several hundreds of millions of years to develop each process of everything from that cell to the present forms would have taken up more than the calculated time assumed; it would have required more than the $1\frac{1}{2}$ billions plus amount. As much of this is statistical and theoretical, errors can slip in because factual bases are not accessible.

As most of the higher organisms must have passed through a very long sequence of intermediate forms, their genealogy would extend over a greater distant past. The conditions on earth for the existence of life were not much below the 2-billion-year mark and might have been below the $1\frac{1}{2}$-billion count, making it appear that the allotted time could not be sufficient for a development in that length of time of the highest form of life, man.

There are scientists who believe for a good part of the early period of the earth's evolution, when it was supposed that the cell was evolving, there were really no cells evolving but that the period was sterile. Also, some think the cell was not evolved first, but that the fundamental property or properties of living systems must have appeared in other forms antedating the cells. These observations make discrepancy obvious in the various calculations and hypotheses. Besides, we know that heat tends to destroy adhesion and cohesion; if we had a "hot thin soup" in the days of life's origin, there could not be any cells or molecules forming, because the excessive heat would have prevented their amassing. The temperatures had to be favorable for life to start its affinitive abode evolvements. The "hot thin soup" was not eternal, who created it?

In our many studies of life and evolution, the sense of a progressive development of organic life forms from the simple rudimentary to the highest, most complex forms, despite gaps and much missing evidences, is held, and all of the studies are made in this mental atmosphere. Such an evolution is practical, but when we consider that since the splitting of the atom many convictions were changed or abandoned, it appears possible that, some day in the future, someone may prove that the processes of change, in each period of the earth's evolution, were infused into the organisms, each with its own kind of life and form, by God. The Bible mentions a similarity when it says God created all forms of life, each in its kind and according to its kind. Such a probability and possibility are practical. Chance, hazard, confusion, chaos, caprice, and disorder never existed at that period of creation. Such conditions appear only in the sense of man's mind but not in reality, because in Nature everything follows law and order. The universe, life, and man were not fortuitous. Everything has come for some reason and purpose, by plan, law, and order.

II

Evolution is a series of events and not an innate intelligence. It is the development of things from rudimentary conditions to more highly organized results, and it is the hypothesis of the origin of the world and of living creatures. There are two kinds of evolution: the absolute or atheistic evolution, which denies God's part in the world; and the mitigated or a limited evolution, which acknowledges Divine intervention. Both are theories and have not been completely proven. Atheistic evolution, the ideas of which have been rejected by everyone except the materialist, though being an unverified theory, is still accepted by and considered as a fact by some people whose minds are in error. A few facts exist about some form of evolution, but no complete theory of evolution has been scientifically substantiated.

The materialist claims everything began with generating atoms which contained, in germ, all the forces of Nature and produced all of the phenomena and varied beings of the earth by a continued evolution, but he does not tell from whence came these primitive bodies and who endowed them with such wonderful properties. If the atom exists of itself, it is eternal; how does it happen, then, that it is still not completely developed? With these blind elements scattered through space, can he explain the order of the world, even that of the organic and mineral creation? By the accidental union of these atoms, how can he ever arrive at organization, at life, at the birth of those principles which move, develop, and reproduce themselves? If the plant and the animal be only a combined collection of cells and molecules, who brought them together, or how did they come to co-ordinate themselves in so strangely wise a manner? And from where did the blind and dumb organic molecules get the knowledge that they must perpetuate themselves and their creations?

The cosmological argument directly refutes the system of materialism; it is impossible to explain the order and harmony which adorn the world by this fortuitous concourse of blind molecules, and all of the evidence to be seen in this world proves it superabundantly.

To say geometry, celestial mechanism, the principles of physics and chemistry, the intentions of physiology, all of the laws which by simplicity and productive generality cause bewilderment to the learned minds, to say all of this is the work of an industry which ignores itself, which is skillful without willing it, profound without knowing it, realizing universal harmony by an admirable chain of relations which it has established without understanding them, is absurd. To admit that the world is a most marvelous work of art and refuse to admit a Supreme Artist; to recognize an intelligent work and deny the intelligent workman is really the height of absurdity.

The materialistic claim that a chance combination of elements produced the universe is fantastic in its concept. How much chance would you have if you threw all the letters of the alphabet together and tried to produce just one line of Scripture from the Bible, or one line from your favorite novel or poem? If you produced a word, how would you know it was a word if you had not known it beforehand? How, in throwing the letters together, could you try not only to produce a book but also put life into it?

Such stuff is impossible. You would never succeed. Chance as a cause is blind; it neither sets order nor chooses things; it has neither will nor understanding. The universe bears evidence of a cause infinitely powerful, industrious, and intelligent. It is an almighty and infinite power that is not confined to this earth upon which we live, but embraces all of the planets and stars. This cause is God, who made all the laws to govern and regulate space and everything within it, but not to have any power over Him. He is the fountain of life and intellect, the principle of existence, and the source of all goodness. He is like the center of a circle, all within Himself, controlling all without. We see Him manifest Himself in everything and in many ways. To be seen personally, God would have to appear in a visible state, but all things in a visible state are limited by space, and God is above space. The Almighty, in a materialistic state, could not permeate through the spiritual and invisible of the universe, but in spirit and Godly essence He can permeate everything, materialistic or not, and reveal Himself in all processes, evolutionary or otherwise.

After so evident a demonstration of the order which we see presiding over the physical economy of our planet, it would be as unreasonable to admit that the wheels and springs of a watch were made and set together by mere chance as to attribute the direction of the phenomena of Nature to the work of hazard. The earth was intended for man's habitation by the Creator, and everything in Nature obeys the laws comformable to that supreme end, as indicated and determined by that Creator.

The development of a living organism—plant, animal, or man—is in many ways like building a machine designed to perform a definite function. A plan must first be made, and this can only be made by an intelligent being with his attention focused, not only on his past experience, but also on the purpose for which the machine is constructed. Since an impersonal Nature, as atheistic evolution, cannot have such characteristics, we must believe in a Personal God, the One uncaused, self-sufficient, and eternal First Cause.

Science, far from banishing God as a useless hypothesis, proclaims His existence as the fundamental reason and cause of all law and all order, as the necessary basis of all philosophy, and as the only reasonable explanation of Nature.

III

It is ridiculous to imagine that a fatal law of necessity presides over the universe; because blind necessity, being always unchangeable, could never produce the remarkable variety we see in things around us. It is ridiculous to think that this fatal, blind necessity can produce order, free beings, or being itself, without intelligence, beget intelligent beings.

How can Nature aspire fatally to progress and ideal perfection when it is blind? How can it aspire to the ideal which it knows not, which does not exist, and which is nothing but a fantastic hope? And again, how can this ideal, not existing, attract Nature and determine the activity of its power?

The single cell—the amoeba—does not produce life within itself; it was and is endowed with life and instinct by God, and this life and instinct have been passed on to the other cells. These cells, when concerned with different species of life, possess different instincts and properties, both adapted to the particular species and unworkable in others.

There is no evidence of spontaneous generation; organisms seem always to arise from pre-existing organisms of the same species; where any suggestion to the contrary has been fancied, there have been flaws in the experimentation.

The forms of the various animals seem at first sight to be the effect of caprice, and it is frequently difficult to account for the many curious forms in a great number of cases. They appear as products of Darwinian evolution, but, in looking at them at a closer range, you will find that everything is foreseen and combined according to principles which to a great extent science has succeeded in discovering. It is in this close proximity that the soul sees the harmony of Nature, which raises it above the physical world and impresses it with the idea of that Divine Intelligence which directs all that is and all that has ever been.

It is impossible not to see in Nature and through the whole of creation the marks and signs of the infinite wisdom, which, imposing certain elementary laws on matter, so determines them that their most ulterior consequences must ever be in harmony with the preservation of organic life and the well-being of all rational creatures destined to people the earth. It is in these unlooked-for results that the eternal wisdom shines out all the more brilliantly by astonishing us with the vast extent of its conceptions, and by the precision with which it attains all of its ends. Be it a body of man or animal, God foresaw what its actions and habits would be, and in anticipation of such built its various parts. In all the varied organisms and in their myriad connections there is manifest not only the work of an intelligence, but also we see premeditation, reason, grandeur, omniscience, and God Himself.

Evolutionists contend that primitive germs of life could have come to the earth by means of some meteor or by some fragment of a planet in which life existed. If they did, how did they commence there? It is not a question from what planet life came, the question of origin remains the same—how did life commence? Life has not always existed on this earth, nor was it formerly always possible, because during the epoch of the formation of primitive rock no living organism could have subsisted here under the conditions prevailing in that era.

Going out into space, we find a thick band of intense radiation six hundred miles above our earth, which extends possibly to a distance of eight thousand miles into space. This radiation is a thousand times more intense than cosmic rays and has existed for ages. It is a "plasma" of hydrogen gas ionized into negatively charged electrons and positively charged protons. The magnetic field of the earth keeps it about six hundred miles away from us. If it would be dangerous for a man, without specific protection, to go through such a band, how much chance has a cell of life in going through it and coming here? It would be dead matter if it was fortunate enough to get through. Then, another thing, to get here and live a cell would need oxygen. Our atmosphere would have had to be right for its existence at the time, which it was not. And if it was right, then, on its way to this planet, it would have encountered our air blanket miles above the earth and would have got itself burned up before it could have gone very far. There were and are so many hazards to such a cell's travel and existence that it is ridiculous to contemplate life coming here from outer space.

Life did not and could not come here from somewhere else without being created by someone. This someone in the universe gives significance and meaning, call it value if you wish, to existence, and no such sense of value can possibly be in mere lumps of dead matter interacting according to purely mechanical laws. Life does not fit into the universal pattern evolutionists try to build. It keeps its value for everything, dead or alive.

As some of the angles of evolutionary opinions are so absurd in our common-sense world, one wonders why certain learned people stay so stubborn in their errors and keep living in a world of fantasy. In our daily life, if we showed someone an object composed of many parts which concur to produce a useful effect, as a watch for example, and seriously said that the object happened by chance and without intention, he would say we were crazy and had lost our sense of reality; and this is a state of mind those learned persons subsist on.

If evolution, as it is contended, produces because there has been a predisposition, a thought, desire, condition, or a state of things tending to a certain goal, why has it failed for man, who has constantly desired, worked, and fought to live, but not die? Why does he have to die? Why has not evolution done away with death, if it is so obliging in evolving various properties, forms, and functions of life and life itself? The struggle for survival has existed since the beginning of life on earth, why has it failed in removing this condition when the atheist claims it is so intelligent, resourceful, and powerful? For ages man has desired to enjoy a nice crown of hair, why does he have to get bald? Why does evolution work against his desires? Why? Because this atheistic evolution was not invented from an impartial point of view; it was set up, basically, in order to destroy God and the belief in Him, by denying His existence. But a man does not destroy God by denying Him, he destroys himself.

> *Man's touch defiles the lovely things*
> *And ravishes the lands. . . .*
> *That's why God keeps His Heaven*
> *Just beyond our mortal hands!**

I V

The premise upon which the atheistic evolution of the universe is based is a mere supposition that chance was possible due to an upset of order and a clash of causes, each of which was going its own way. The reasoning behind this was to deny the manifestations of God and make an impossibility a possibility. Everyone knows God reveals Himself to man through the material and also the spiritual, but the freethinkers, because of their pride and self-conceit, endeavor to deny Him.

Man has always worshiped some kind of god or gods through the past ages. If such an instinct or realization has always been in human beings, the Almighty must have caused it to be there.

* From "Just Beyond" by Nick Kenny, *Poems to Inspire,* T. S. Denison & Company, Minneapolis.

And human beings are the only ones who have that realization; no other form of animal life has this conception. The understanding of reality is in the human spirit. Man's evolution had a faster pace than that of other things because of his spirituality and his mind filled with intellectual desires lacking in animals and plants. Much of the creation living on earth cannot reason, or express itself steadily, or be firmly fixed in thought or desire; a condition which contradicts some of the attributes of evolution.

At the beginning of our century, when people should have known better than in the four previous centuries, there were some thinkers whose training, it seems, was unadvanced. Among these was Haeckel, a great exponent of Darwinism. When he wrote that atoms were condensations of a simple substance, filling the whole space with unbroken continuity, and that the strain upon the ether from these condensations gave us energy, he was thinking along the lines of least resistance. And in addition, he claimed that ether was a kind of jelly filling all space; and that, though he recognized the existence of Nature, it was to him impenetrable. He called it a phantom and suggested thinkers should not brood over it. In one breath, he advises, he cannot reason Nature out, implying he could not make a decision about it; in another breath, he claims that it was blind evolution which created it, and he was sure of it.

Scrutinizing such writings of the various prominent Darwinists, one finds a medley of seeming contradictions. It is gratifying to witness that many of these theories are passing into oblivion. For instance, by the discovery of the genes, the laws of heredity founded by Mendel, which were established as a fact, Darwinian evolution by the process of natural selection, or variation, has lost considerably. Darwin's reasoning is questionable on this subject; he tried to set up something which did not wholly exist.

The composition of cell protoplasm is known to the scientist, but he has not been successful in synthesizing protoplasm in the laboratory; nor has he been able to determine why it possesses that property which we call "life." Life cannot be produced in a test tube. The fact should be taken into consideration that most astronomers are also rather skeptical of the presence of life on any neighbor planet except our own. As to other solar systems with planets, which might have served as a source of life, none are known, but if they do exist, they must be so far distant that any germs of life coming from them to the earth through the extremely severe conditions of outer space, after many years of wandering and travel, would be dead and useless.

An end supposes the choice, disposition, and direction of the means. In Nature these ends are obtained and useful effects realized; but we may ask are these effects intended? Are the ends intentional, calculated? Of course they are! But we must admit an Intelligent Cause knows those effects beforehand and intends to produce them. The common sense of the world at large protests any denial of such. The First Cause of order always precedes the immediate physical cause of effect, and it is and was always an Intelligent Cause. This Intelligent Cause is God, whose end it was to put life upon this globe, utilizing cells and organisms to reflect its effects.

Referring to some of the wonders of evolution, let us make a few statements and queries. Under the influence of the sun, leaves decompose the carbon dioxide so prejudicial to animal life, and absorb the carbon into their tissues, in return, giving back to the air purified oxygen. How did evolution establish this equilibrium, which animal respiration and combustion of every kind tends to destroy, and restore the air to its native purity? How did evolution know that one needed something for its use, and another should provide it? In the processes of reproduction (as in plants), how did evolution know that bees or other means, living or not, must be employed? How did it know all the hazards a plant must survive so that it endowed it with a great fecundity so that its species should not die out? Whence came that directive power that certain plants, too weak of themselves, could attach themselves to others for help or protection?

In the boundless variety of plants there is a certain stability and fixity of type which nothing can destroy. One generation succeeds another, thousands, nay millions, of individuals disappear, but the specific type remains. Seeds and grains, left four or five thousand years ago in the Egyptian tombs, compared with those of today, have not changed a bit. Why? Because it was an intelligence, that First Cause, which directed their evolution with such art and perfect wisdom, and graded everything to live in its own sphere of existence.

V

It is an error in the scientific world, when dispensing information about the origin of life and of the universe, to take theories and treat them as facts. Theories are only likelihoods; facts are actual knowledge. If a fact is to be a fact, it must be a 100 per cent fact and it should not be adulterated. Keep theories and consider them for what they are until they are proven completely and thus made factual, because a fact in science must be absolutely exact or it is not a fact. Considering some evolutionary hypotheses as factual is disparaging to scientific knowledge, and it is a cause of much discord in the lives of men.

The use of the word "fact" in wrong instances or connections produces a misleading mental state in those who are not cautious, for it possesses too much of a positive sound. A fact is factual today and tomorrow; it is not something that may need further refinement, alteration, or abandonment.

No scientist should jump to conclusions, because he still has much to learn. Using theories as facts because they are supported by an abundance of circumstantial evidence is leaning too much on assumption. Atoms and cells, as ultimate things with an abundance of circumstantial evidence, appeared factual years ago, but they have been disproven. Much of theoretical scientific knowledge is only statistical. Such actions by a scientist reveal he has faith in his or his colleague's work. He believes in it, though it may be proven false someday. But other persons who have faith in opposition to his ideas he criticizes and ridicules as superstitional ignoramuses. Because he thinks he is right, everybody should listen to him; if not, no matter if your education is superior to his, you are a nobody. He makes himself the "ultimate thing," by asserting what is not known as known. Before the splitting of the atom, philosophies were erected on such a basis; today, the rationalist is repeating the same errors, building not on actual facts but on suggestive hypotheses. These, being considered as factual, are responsible for the "superiority complex" of the atheists. Frustrated, these people, seeing many of their former contentions fizzling away, are desperate to regain lost ground. They are trying to resurrect Darwin and some of his discarded theories so they can return to the old reasoning, because they see no other way out but to recognize God, His existence and omnipotence. To get around the Almighty, they resort to the pet phrase "the fortuitous concourse of atoms" and to assumption. The more science advances, the more rapidly "fortuitous" shrivels and disappears. As the aboriginal nebula disproves the "fortuitous," so will other things disprove the assumption in their evolution. There are no wonders or startling effects in natural law and in the universe, without a mind, a reason, a plan, and order back of them.

Evolvement of inorganic molecules into organic; proteins, amino acids, protoplasms, chlorophyls, enzymes, etc., are nothing else but agents of life, and not life itself, neither are they creators of life. They cannot evolve into growing complexities, if they have not been endowed for that purpose. They merely work within the bounds of matter and earthly life's necessity and with certain directives. The existence of endowed or infused powers, as in elements, organic molecules, and all living things, is not questioned. These powers were put there by a Creator, and all to act in their different and specific ways.

The pronouncements of science are not final and they are far from becoming final, because they are perpetually being modified and supplemented.

Writers on natural science and physics travel outside their branch of work when they carry their questionable and unconfirmed ideas and teachings into the domain of philosophy or religion.

It is easy for a scientist to work out complete mathematical and physicochemical formulae for matter without life, but for matter with life it appears as a hopeless task. They have tried in their laboratories to produce life by reproducing primeval conditions, as per their theories, but all attempts were fruitless. They tell us how the processes of life progress and what the developments are, but cannot tell us what life is and who put it here or on the other planets, if any. The mystery of life is not solved, no matter how men theorize or what experiments produce; no one has ever created life in a laboratory. It must be said life is not the result of combined constituents of organic matter, but that matter is merely a medium through which life expresses itself.

God does not hinder man from studying the universe or what life is; how they work and why they are. God did not advise man that he must investigate everything; much He had restricted by distances, sizes, forces, and other things. He put man here to work out his personal problems and to look to his salvation, and he should leave the rest to His Divine Providence.

The Roman Catholic Church is not an enemy of science. She does not deny the wonderful works of God in His providential influence upon the creation and evolvement of the universe and of life. But it cannot approve the arrogance of some "earthly" scientists, who ignore the power and wisdom in evolution which is from "above," and supplement it with powers of blind and dumb forces evident here "below."

The First Cause

A HAPPY COINCIDENCE does not prove a desired end; but when a large number of agents scattered through space, indifferent to any kind of position, are united together and disposed with order and symmetry; when they are so adapted as to concur to a common end to some useful effect, then reason tells us that, in order to produce that union, that adaptation, that harmony, there must be a cause; and it tells us again, for such an adaptation, for such a system so widely combined, a blind cause could never suffice. It must needs be an intelligent cause. Why? Because all the varied parts of that system, being at first dispersed and indifferent to every kind of position, could not unite together, or arrange themselves in such order, or adapt themselves to a particular end, were they not chosen, disposed of, and adapted by an intelligent cause which alone selects, guides, and adapts; because, again, such a cause alone can know the end and proportion the means to that end; such a cause alone can single out from a thousand different means those that are necessary and arrange them in the required order; such a cause alone, in fine, can adapt them in order to produce this end, or that result.

And the long series of contingent effects and of perishable beings which succeed each other in this world obliges man's intelligence to recognize this cause, the First Cause, a cause not produced but subsisting by virtue of its own power. The order of this world, the plan of organized beings, fashioned and governed with so much art, reveals to us the nature of this First Cause; because, to have conceived this order, it must have had an intelligence sufficiently comprehensive to embrace in a single glance all of its least details; it must have been sufficiently powerful to realize that order, and to preserve it.

As intelligence is a faculty of a spirit, we cannot conceive thinking and planning without a personality that does the work. A spiritual entity which can think, plan, endow, produce, and govern everything.

A simple body—cell—cannot have life from itself, so far as it is material, for matter lacks essential nature; this matter will not give form to itself or insert a soul into itself. Nothing can exist if there is no spiritual power. The resourcefulness of life to accomplish its purpose and ends is a demonstration of the all-pervading, intelligent and powerful Spirit—our Personal God. Animal wisdom tells irresistibly of this kind Creator who infused instinct into otherwise helpless creatures. Their environment and mode of life and the mysterious techniques cannot be explained by adaptation, they were bestowed by the Creator. The most minute crawler is a creation of art, which He only can comprehend.

Geology reveals order has prevailed from the beginning of time. Chance could not explain this, but the First Cause could. This First Cause was the first adequate cause of order, it was not an immediate physical cause; it was an act of an intelligence. You do not look in a machine or in an atom smasher for an intelligence, but in the person who devised and put them together.

When the First Cause created things, He also gave us different natures. A dog has a dog nature, a monkey has a monkey nature, a man has human nature, etc. Human nature answers the query "Who is it?" while other natures answer "What is it?" These natures of things tell us what they are; human nature— a person—tells us who he is. To consider man and his nature as something of matter, and to ignore his spiritual part, is to take a view that is limited and lacking in total reality. It is a very limited and one-sided view. Material forces may contribute to some ordered effects, but they do not suffice of themselves. If we have any imperfections in man or his nature, or anywhere else in Nature, they have their reasons for existing.

How can you persist in living and attributing everything to the effects of happy chance or to a fortuitous, unpredetermined gathering together of agents, when everywhere and in everything the hand of the artist, the Hand of God, who was the First Cause, is evident and manifest, too visible to be doubted? You must reflect more, to see God everywhere, and after an honest endeavor truth and reason will be yours.

Much of the energy of this world is being lost day by day in the form of heat. It is not destroyed, but escapes into outer space. This, in time, will produce a condition of complete stagnation, and all motion will cease. The universe is in a constant process of deterioration and degradation, proving it is not eternal and will have an end. If the universe had existed for all eternity, it would have been reduced to the stage of utter stagnation long centuries ago. The fact that it has not, and there is still plenty of energy left in this world, proves that the world is not eternal;

that it began to exist in time and therefore had an origin, a Creator, a First Cause.

Because of the marvelous unity everywhere in the universe, science has completely established that this First Cause must be a Single Cause. And this Single Cause is nothing else but wonderful God, who is not only wonderful, but also good and merciful, and all-powerful and everlastingly solicitous.

Life and Existence

A DROP OF WATER taken from the ocean by the rays of the sun and reduced to vapor floats on the wind and is carried off into faraway places, where it falls on the earth in the form of rain, and nourishes and fructifies the earth's plants. And then, carried away by some stream, it returns again to its place of origin, the ocean, to begin another cycle of metamorphosis, and this cycle goes on and on.

A plant grows from a seed, produces flowers, fruit, and seeds, according to its own mode of reproduction and its own kind, and then withers and dies. The seeds take up the cycle and repeat it, and the cycle goes on and on, while the formation of the flowers, fruit, and seeds undergoes cycles of its own in the meantime.

Butterflies and moths pass through four stages. The female lays the eggs and these hatch into caterpillars. The latter go into a dormant stage, either as cocoon or chrysalis, then the adult winged insect wakes up and breaks forth from the sleeping pupa stage to fly about and lay eggs and start the cycle over again. And each stage undergoes its own cycle, containing other cycles of development and existence of the various parts that make up the stage.

We are men and human beings. We come from our parents and are endowed by God with a soul and a sex. We develop to maturity and then decline to old age. We pass a cycle of existence, which begins from the former cycles of our parents and ends at the time of our decease; in fact, it does not end, but passes on into other cycles of existence beyond our demise.

Everything in the universe, at the time of creation, started its cycle of existence from the First Cause, God, and ended in another cycle just beginning, or in some other one which had also been started by the First Cause. And this process, having started, has gone on and on, and will go on until the end of the universe. Some of these cycles are of a short duration, while others take a longer time; their existence is varied; they all arise from former cycles and continue into new or existing cycles. No abrupt ends occur. Everything passes into something else. All pass their existence within other larger cycles of which they are or become a part, and these go on within others, which are still larger, until the final cycle, the largest of all and encompassing them all, ends where it began, in the former First Cause, God.

You have been born and come from the cycles of your parents' existence, and during your cycle of life every time you come to an end of anything, you find a new beginning. And you find that many things you have witnessed have had their cycles of existence during your lifetime; they have come into being from other sources, from other cycles, and ended in other cycles of use or decay; and most of these passed into other cycles, and these within others; all within or passing through your cycle and during its existence.

And your cycle of life, in the meantime, spent its duration within the cycle of your community, which also consisted of other series of other beings and things. And this community's era, developing from other origins, grew and passed off into the development of a state's cycle. And the state's cycle sprang from the existence of a combine of many communities and spaces, and developed and progressed into a country's cycle of existence. Then this national cycle, covering and being a part of many other cycles within its borders and beyond, issued itself into that of the world's affairs; and the world's doings and existence, being part of and encircled by that of the universe, which finally terminates in God, the Final End of all things. There is no other end for anything. The whole thing appears like a spiral within a spiral within a spiral, and continuing on, all within one great circle.

Within these cycles of existence, we have an evolution which is limited to the cycle of the thing or the being; it does not create anything but merely develops the capacities of the thing or being. This development has its limitations, dependent upon those capacities and the utility of the properties of the thing, or being. In considering these capacities or properties, we must not forget that, besides our senses and instincts with which we were endowed by God, many of our capacities were not acquired or developed, but were similarly bestowed by the Creator.

So many exacting conditions are necessary for existence on this earth that these conditions could not possibly exist in proper relationship by chance, or prove that life here is an accident. The resourcefulness of life to accomplish its purposes is a manifestation of an all-pervading Intelligence.

As the keys of a piano are arranged so each key gives out its own particular sound, and, when played in groups and at different speeds, they give out sounds of accord or discord; so is man, in body; and animal and plant, so placed in this world to do each its own particular duty, and to work in combination for good or evil. Everything is placed here by God to function for some particular need of existence.

What life is no man has fathomed. It has neither weight nor dimensions, but it does have force, as a growing root will crack a rock. Nature did not create life; fire-blistered rocks and a salt-less sea could not meet the necessary requirements. Who, then, has put it here, if not the Creator of All?

Life

LIFE IS THE PROPERTY of a being which enables it to grow, move, breathe, react to stimulant or irritant, and reproduce its own kind. Some living things possess all of these attributes; some possess only a few. Life is a conflict psychologically, and all living things must find ways of adjustment. Life presents organization; it has the power of perpetuating and reproducing itself.

When writing about the origin of life and of the world, atheists concoct an idea which seems plausible, adopt it, and build a story around it. Fiction is composed in the same manner. There are no actual facts or verified knowledge. They explain that a combination of molecules from the primeval ooze spontaneously produced life. If such a combination was possible, it did not produce life but the processes which reflected life with which they were endowed by the Creator, the First Cause. In our modern existence, this can be illustrated by the following example: A working machine and its motor are not electricity; their processes are the result of a force given them by electricity, and this force did not come to them spontaneously, it was created by an intelligence, man, to run the motor and the machine.

Spontaneous generation and natural selection have been discarded, leaving nothing for the atheists to do but to admit to a creation by an Omnipotent Power. This is too much for them to stomach, so they are trying a return to spontaneous generation by organic and inorganic molecules; and to natural selection, an insufficient theory, and are building up a fantastic hypothesis on the basis of something that never happened, so they can avoid admitting that there is a God and that there was a creation.

Life comes from life and not from any combination of molecules. No matter how any combine may produce a process or structure of life, it does not produce life or the intelligence needed to be able to use that life, or to make organisms conform to their special living forms and functions.

Life does not come from crystals. Living beings' attributes are different from those of crystals; life is action in all of its phases. And amino acids and other compounds are only constituents of organisms and the expressers of life's processes, but not the life which makes use of them.

A cell or a molecule of life could not come to this earth from outer space, because conditions make it impossible. Distance alone is a great hazard. Nearby stars do not possess water in the liquid state to maintain a living cell. A comet, meteor, or meteorite cannot carry a life germ, because they have not and cannot maintain an atmosphere; they are too cold to carry liquid water, and they are unprotected from all the deadly radiations and heat from the stars, and the frigid cold of remote space.

Heat and radiation near a star's surface would break up and separate all molecules constituting protoplasm of any germ traveling near that star; also, the molecular aggregates called proteins, which are very tender, would be easily affected by any adverse conditions. This radiation which would endanger any spore of life traveling through space, or near our earth, is a great potent danger to any life. We must not forget that we have countless numbers of star galaxies which have their own bands of radiation penetrating into space; some with powers more dangerous and of greater menace than anything near our earth.

The atheist seldom tries to explain the origin of life by a direct approach; he usually uses a roundabout and illusive method with high-sounding words to start his explanations. A believer in God does not get shocked because he tells him that life was created in the sea, or on land, before man. The believer knows it did; his Bible told him so before he ever heard the assertions of the atheist.

The great bodies of water were formed probably one to one and one-half billion years ago as sweet water. This is the upper possible limit. Then salt began to be deposited into the seas. If the oceans existed for a longer period, they would now all be as salty as the Dead Sea or the Great Salt Lake.

The primeval oceans may have accumulated all sorts of complicated organic matter at a certain early epoch, and their molecules could have united to form elementary compounds, but these would not be farther away from producing life than the synthetic substances produced artificially in laboratories. The spark of life had to be given to the chemical constitution of the certain cells, and they had to be endowed with properties to do their work, just as the Creator planned them to do. No matter how and in what way or form their progress was, there had to be an Intelligence, a First Cause, to guide and direct the creation which later culminated in man, whom God endowed with a soul and intelligence.

The further processes of evolution themselves reveal that blind matter could not evolve the wonderful forms, effects, and functions that followed, but the hand of a Creator was observed in everything. The molecules which life used were molecules of matter and not those of intelligence, reason, and wisdom. The simple forms of life, as viruses, were composed of complicated molecules of carbon, hydrogen, oxygen, and nitrogen atoms, but these molecules did not, and do not, generate life proper.

If the atheists' contentions that there were molecules of life at the beginning of the living world were true, some of those molecules should be present today. One or a few of one kind of molecule of life could not make such a varied world of living things. If there were such agents, there would have had to be a large amount of them and of many different varieties. They could not all disappear into the past, some would remain today. But as things are not as they have been pictured, we must pass them by as theoretical fancies.

Without oxygen, life could not exist on this earth; man and animal must breathe it to live. Plants, by the medium of photosynthesis and chlorophyll, change carbon dioxide into oxygen. Men and animals inhale it and exhale the carbon dioxide, which again the plants use, causing what is known as the carbon cycle. Besides, photosynthesis is instrumental in producing food for the plants to live on, and in causing plants to produce food for man and animal. The Creator, in His wisdom, endowed plant life with chlorophyll and the processes of photosynthesis, to enable it to serve man. Plants are fixed to a place; animals are limited to space, but man is not limited to place or space, he is limited by time. Plants and animals are here to serve him.

When we observe how sound is graded from the lowest to the highest tone; how the mechanisms of our hearing and tasting organs are graded in their construction; how light is graded to wave lengths; how every species of animal is graded by breed, characteristics, natures, habits, etc.; how man is graded by his make-up, color, intelligence, character, etc.; how every kind of plant life is classed and graded by its growth, flower, fruit, habitat, etc.; and how gradation is evident in almost everything we meet with, it behooves us to consider the possibility that evolution had nothing to do with their origins, as it is assumed in some present-day contentions. Rather it is clear that God created life in graded beings and things, which could exist only at the stage which earth's evolution had attained at the specific period, and then banished it at His will to replace it with other advanced life forms when conditions seemed more improved and more suitable to the advanced forms. Those gradations were of different stages, and each stage could be merged into the other only with the impulse of a Power from the outside. They reveal the direct action of a Being at the specific points in evolution. As to the present era of earth's evolvement, it seems that it could have been possible to have forms of life created in graded structures and types, with man evolving as the highest masterpiece of God's creation.

If man had evolved from the same molecules as the rest of living beings, though there could be a difference in forms and structures, flesh should have a similarity to the original molecules. But there is not any similarity; there is a great difference between all flesh, be it of man, animal, fish, or bird. Each has its own kind and differs from the other.

Irritability, motility, growth, reproduction are properties of life. In irritability, we find life sets up a special function in certain parts of a living body; it acts as a vigilant in those parts and reacts to any sudden irritant or stimulus present there. It is like an accumulated electrical charge set on guard, which, when a stimulus or irritant influences it, affects the immediate organs or structures of the organism. While sending an impulse to the brain, it causes them to react, permitting time for the soul and its life processes to take over. These sensory outposts, or reflex centers, exist while life is in the system. When life and soul leave, they disappear soon after.

Matter without life merely keeps its adhesion and cohesion because of the amount of favorable heat it possesses at the moment. Excess of heat causes it to lose its form and its adhesion and cohesion. Matter with life, organic matter, keeps its adhesion and cohesion because of life in it, and the soul gives it form. When the life and soul leave, the form and matter disintegrate.

Our existence is like a sentence, which is not only composed of the objective; it has its subjective and other parts also. The world and the life on it are composed of more than what an atheistic science finds in them; they have more than mere objectivity.

Life and Intelligence

LIFE IS NOT A SERIES of accidents or a mere sequence of chance happenings. Living things obey laws; they follow a plan; they show evidence of design and purpose. In all living processes, there is some operating power of a mysterious character, some guiding principle. If the series of living beings is eternal, this series cannot exist of itself; it is entirely composed of produced beings, and itself entirely produced, so therefore it demands a cause which is not itself, but outside itself. This cause is the fountainhead of life and lies in the non-physical world.

Everything possessing life possesses a status of evolution in a limited sense, and does not go beyond that. Agents necessary for development must be present and available. If their availability should be curtailed, things—man also—would deteriorate and turn to a low standard of existence; viz.: vegetables, by proper cultivation and fertilization, can be improved to a larger and better state; man, by proper food, education, environment, and living, can make himself rank high above the savages.

Every animal has its own instincts; its own cunning artifices, whether for attack or defense; and certain faculties; but it has no reason which can abstract and generalize, which understands spiritual things, absolute truths, and universal principles. Their instincts tell them the "how" and not the "why" of things; and enable them to learn only limited things.

What concerns man most about life is human life and intelligence. Man wants to know what makes him live and why. What is the purpose of it all? In Divine Revelations, he will find the answers to these questions of the human mind and heart, because religion has its revelations and traditions, as science has its logic and mathematics; but logic and mathematics are not science. They are necessary to science, just as revelations and traditions are indispensable to religion and the Church.

There is a contention that, without life experience, it is impossible to do, or know, the difference between one thing and another. In part it is true, and in part it is false. Men, as well as animals, are endowed—remember, endowed—with an instinctive intelligence, and they use it in many ways. Man, as a babe, knows that he must eat, and so places everything in his mouth; birds know the art and what materials are needed to build their nests; sea animals, on hatching from their eggs, know how to swim; and if these eggs hatch on the beach, they know, after leaving the shell, where the water is and how to swim in it; eels will find their way from the continents to the Sargasso Sea, there to breed and die; and their offspring will know when and how to go to the waters of the continents from which their parents came.

Those who claim that experience founds all of our knowledge, if they would study man and animals, would find they have overlooked the knowledge which God has bestowed upon His creatures. This knowledge is bestowed at birth, and not acquired or developed. In this knowledge they live until they are more mature and able to express it in sign, word, or action. This certain knowledge, as perception, volition, or will, discerning and distinguishing, etc., is instinctive. These are the qualities coming from the soul, as the body, being weak and undeveloped, has to take time to build up and strengthen itself. It must mature to the point where it can try to express its ideas to the outside world and to itself, in sound, sign, or action, and then accept things from experience. If man was born in the wilds of the jungle with the opportunity to live without any other human near him, he would develop his instinctive knowledge without experience and know how to satisfy his primary needs as well as some animals I have observed, which, brought up in certain ignorance, when tested for what knowledge they possessed in certain matters, unerringly acted out and performed the things they never were instructed in and never had a chance to see.

In plants, the endowment with certain properties is revealed when certain parts of the plants develop or mature to a certain point and then express a certain property. A flower will follow the sun; it may open at definite hours of the day or night; it may be able to catch insects and devour them, etc.

The importance of instinctive knowledge in human life is beyond exaggeration. We find it contributes to many things, among which are art, music, literature, religion, science, and philosophy. This intelligence is rooted into a world that is not built of atoms; it is an infinitesimal part of the Supreme Intelligence.

The human is so constituted that he cannot fail to intellectualize his experiences. He can visualize, while an animal cannot. He thinks, but his thought is not a chemical change in the brain, it is not a quality of matter. Science shows that there are no connections between thought and the chemical elements of the brain matter. Though thought may have an association with brain matter, as the heart and brain have with the body; a reaction in the brain matter, in whole or in part, may bring forth thoughts that are just memories of former experiences, but these are old, no new ones are created that have no affinity to the old. No thoughts are expressed that have not been in the mind beforehand. The brain does not generate thoughts and ideas, but is only an instrument of thoughts or ideas, as the eye is to light, for the soul.

Our intelligence can, by its natural light of reason, and from the consideration of created things, enable us to attain to a "sure" awareness of the Supreme Intelligence, God.

The Soul

I

WHEN A PERSON has the knowledge of how things occur, it is simple for him to understand, but when he does not know, he expresses doubt or disbelief; because his knowledge is short and lacking much of inquiry. When he adds prejudice and bias to his reasoning, he hinders his mind from seeing things in the right light. The younger the thinker is, the more impulsive, censorious, and impatient are his arguments. Rejection of things because one does not understand is unwise and narrow-minded. Many of us do not understand the intricacies of television or the radio, or even the simplicities of the phonograph, and yet we do not therefore refuse to accept them. When we make use of an intelligence honestly, it will discover the other intelligence in the universe.

Experiences as in "extrasensory perception" are brushed aside by non-believers as mere coincidences. They do not like to be shaken out of their shell of materialism by recognizing such phenomena. They would rather, like the proverbial ostrich, hide their heads in the sands of self-sufficiency and bias than admit that there exists a realm beyond matter. When one studies a great number of these experiences, they lose all appearance of being accidental. There are indications that something lies behind these happenings. Something that has the power to reach beyond space and time, something that transcends the physical law, something demonstrating itself as of a spiritual rather than of a physical system. In some of these "experiences" we cannot assume that subconscious clairvoyance moves the heavy matter about, the latter must be propelled by some spiritual entity, either by the latter's power, or, it being under the exerted power of a person who may be in a hysterical, or concentrated, mental state. These "experiences" are all spiritual phenomena and not the work of blind and dumb molecules.

When you dream, you see, hear, speak, smell, and touch. You are conscious of your senses. But you do not see with your eyes or hear with your ears, and the same is true of the other senses. How can you explain this?

When awake, you can see spots before your eyes. Medical science explains them as being on the lens or retina of your eye. If you press your eye gently, you may see jagged lines appear on your eye's lens; or, looking intensely at something, you may see the image move. If you look with your eye, how come you can look into your eye, because such is the process if you are watching the spots on your lens? You do not see with your eye! It is merely a gadget—like the lens of a camera—which brings in the picture to the brain. You do not hear with your ears! They are only instrumental in carrying sound to your brain. You do not taste with your tongue; smell with your nose; or feel with your hands. All just receive and send the impressions to the brain.

What intelligence is there in the brain that can see, hear, and know what is coming in? What intelligence is there that can, at the receiving moment, make an instantaneous proper answer? The brain is not endowed with knowledge, it is only a receiving and sending-out set. It is the soul! It is the soul which is not material or mechanical, or just a brain activity. It is something that is apart from the brain. For matter cannot reason and make decisions, but a soul can, because it was endowed from its source with intelligence and reasoning power.

When we get an impression, thought, symbol, etc., in our minds, there must be something there to know what things come in and how to respond or manage them. There must be someone who has the power to think and who is the fountain and center of all of our intellectual activity; who also knows values, be they important, serious, or humorous.

When thinking, we have a continual succession of ideas; some are excited anew, others are changed or totally disappear. There is, therefore, some cause of these ideas, whereon they depend, which produces and changes them. This cause must be a substance; but, as there is no corporeal or material substance, it appears, therefore, that the cause of ideas is an incorporeal, active substance or spirit. It is a spirit, the nature of which you cannot perceive, but only the effects it produces. This spirit is not the mind; it is the soul wherein the mind is seated and which is the entity behind the mind, which controls the mind and life. Mind and life, in turn, control man's body.

The soul functions through the brain and nervous system of the body. All sense impressions do not register as they do on a photographic plate, but there is that intelligent entity, the soul, endowed with its instincts, that recognizes and understands them and knows how to dispose of them. It always makes one aware of the existence of things within or without us and around us.

The soul is the principle by which we live and move and have our being. It forms and perpetuates our identity. It has intellectual conceptions and functions of reason and judgment, independent of material organs. It grasps what our senses cannot reach and knows the difference between good and evil. It thinks of justice and of truth, and perceives the connection existing between premises and conclusions.

The soul of man comes into existence only by a direct creative act of God; it is spiritual and cannot be produced by matter; nor is it generated by human parents. It is a manifestation of the infinite realm of the Spirit, or God.

As man, at the time of his origin, was endowed with a soul, the mind also was endowed with a certain capacity for thought. This capacity did not develop gradually by evolution. It was put there in a complete state. But man, not having an accumulation of knowledge or the state of education, the environment and living conditions of modern times, could use this capacity only in a limited way. Even though Modern Man has a mind richly in possession of advanced thought, nevertheless he has not used up its capacity to the fullest as yet.

II

Man is a duality, composed of body and soul. The soul is his unique human individuality. His body is a machine, and the soul its operator. This spirit of man belongs to an order of being essentially different from, and superior to, that of matter, even though that matter be of immeasurable mass. The life which the soul possesses it will never lose, because it is part of that entity, the soul. The latter is a creation of God and not a product of evolution; it does not fall within the province of any natural science.

Presently, scientists have admitted that the physical concept of man, which prevailed in their intellectual circles since the rise of materialism, is now thoroughly disproved. They admit there is something definitely extraphysical about humans; that there is an order of reality in human life not subject to the laws of time and space. They have verified the essential foundation upon which the spiritual philosophy of man was originally erected. It is from orthodox science and the conservative scientist that we have the main opposition; they fear a division in Nature, a dualism like that of body and soul, so much that they refuse to look at any evidence which would suggest such a duality.

In former centuries, people held notions of man being the center of the universe, but it was the men of the Church, like Copernicus, Galileo, Descartes, Columbus, and others, who proved they were wrong. The Church, per se, did not discourage or prohibit the advance of science and discovery. In fact, it was the Catholics who led in these efforts, and the world owes much to their work and discoveries.

Materialists work hard to develop atheistic evolution and erroneous philosophies about man, but they have not advanced much since the days of materialism's inception. In fact, their work has retrograded; their statements have been arbitrary and devoid of all foundation. On the other side, their opponents also work hard to disprove all the false contentions created by materialists. They have had more success in their labors; they have developed a series of convincing arguments to demonstrate the existence and some of the attributes of God, as well as of the soul. Revelation and tradition are ever-present to support them, but the apathy of their coreligionists hinders their progress. These coreligionists are very materialistic in their behavior and living; they do not want to be conscious of their higher significance; their thoughts and aspirations are not directed toward their soul life; and its continuance after death is ignored until it is too late.

The welfare of the soul should take predominance over the body, because man is made of something more than flesh, blood, and bones; because he is also the spirit which animates and directs his body and gives dignity and meaning to his life. Comparing man to an automobile, we would say his body represents the car; his life, the motor; and his soul, the driver.

Man is something more than mind. He feels and thinks; beauty appeals. Poetry and music stir him. He makes judgments and knows good as well as evil. Ecstasies, passions, and aspirations are of importance to him. He has desires and purposes, and believes in free will. You cannot reduce all of this to measurement and analysis, but can learn much in observing their effects. Emotion and intuition are a vital part of him, to ignore them is to have a biased and unfair view of human life and of the soul which dominates all.

The soul is the "person" in the body who sleeps and not the body; who eats and thinks, who has toothaches and ecstasies and who loves. He is the vital principle of the body. Man is not his soul; body and soul unite into one unit to make man.

The soul is spiritual, it moves and directs itself. Matter cannot modify its own state; it cannot move without first being moved, and it cannot change its direction of motion after once it is moved. Another agent has to be present to move it or change the direction of its motion, but not of the soul, it is free.

When we feed the body we do not feed the soul. Being created by an eternal Spirit, God, in His own likeness, and being endowed with eternity, it does not need food. Of the mental faculties of the soul, the mind is part of the infinite intellect of God, it cannot be reconstructed by our chemical and physical laws, and it is not similar to that of other creatures. Animals are endowed with their own form of thinking; man with his own. Man has not developed his intelligence as something new in this world, he has simply acquired the capacity to reflect a ray of the Universal Spirit, the Universal Intelligence.

Man's eye is limited to light, it is useless in the dark; the soul in this life must use a body and a brain to express itself.

It is proven that man does not look from his eye, but from some place in back of the eye organ; that the eye serves as a camera lens to bring images and sights to the brain. What sees these if it is not your soul? My left eye was damaged some years ago, leaving a dark space running up and down through the middle of my eye's lens. I can place my sight to either side of the dark column and look through one side at a time, or look through both sides at the same time. Also, I can place my sight behind the dark space and study its size and shade. This all proves I do not see with my eye, but from the interior in back of the eye, and it makes me conscious of myself, the soul.

A living being and a whirlpool are pictured to be alike. The whirlpool is permanent in form, only the particles of water which compose it are constantly changing. The water which enters it is whirled around, at the same time it becomes part of the whirlpool, until it leaves at another spot and other water takes its place. While there is an interchange of water, the individuality of the whirlpool remains because of the invisible force that maintains it; so, with a living being, its body and constituents are constantly changing, but its form and individuality are maintained by the invisible force, or entity, the soul. If it was not for this soul, it would disintegrate.

I I I

Man possessed of soul has something more than animal instinct; he has the power of reason and an intuitive, unfailing response, which is a planted knowledge of the Divine. And the fact that man can use this knowledge and conceive the idea of God is itself a unique proof of the existence of a Supreme Being. This endowed knowledge of the Divine was caused by God, and the effect of this realization is religion.

Unbeliever, would you like to materialize God so that you can believe? Do you want to see Him bodily to satisfy your ego? As you cannot see God, do you see "Man"? No! What you see is a body or machine through which the spirit, or soul, manifests itself, but you cannot see the soul, the real man!

You have a soul, which is you and not your body; it is you who is reading, listening, or thinking; you do not see your real self and you wish to have the Almighty appear in the form of matter! How can you demand such a thing when you cannot materialize yourself, outside of your body? You cannot even describe yourself, and you expect a description of the Creator?

When I allude to man's body as a machine, I do so simply for illustration, because a machine which lives, grows, takes in nourishment, reconstructs itself, and tries to keep in balance with its intakes and output, really is not a machine but something more sublime; and, most of all, these operations of the human body are not products of atheistic evolution, but are the endowments of the Creator, governed by the soul.

Because a person cannot feel himself separated in parts; because he cannot focus himself into his soul and gaze inside his body and see each as a separate entity, it is hard for him to realize the duality of body and soul. To some, the study of eye effects brings a little comprehension; to others, it must be said, you cannot get inside of something when you are already there. You have no soul, except that you are the conscious soul, and you have a body upon which you are always gazing. It is not correct for you to think or say, "I have a soul." Rather you should say, "I am the soul and I have a body." Your conscious self is the characteristic of your soul, of you.

Your soul expresses itself to you in your sensation of well-being, outside of your sensation of touch. In your advanced age, you will remember how your spirit felt when you were young, and in your old age you find no difference. You find there is no change or aging in any way except in the body. The whole reflection is of a thing unchangeable. The soul does not age!

The soul has many faculties, among which are imagination, memory, understanding, will, etc., and also virtues, among which are Faith, Hope, and Charity. These are infused virtues and are supernatural; they are not acquired by repeated acts of our own.

There is also an attribute the soul possesses when one is asleep, whereby it is capable of perception of distant scenes, of communications with distant persons, of temporarily leaving a dormant body, and even receiving messages from the spiritual world. When awake, it is casually telepathic, but unlike God, who is completely and universally telepathic.

The way some people, in these days of more advanced knowledge, concern themselves with the existence of the soul makes them objects of derision. Those who cannot disprove the spiritual entity of man, or God, resort to ridicule and mockery. If they did not evade the facts or reasons, they would not hide behind travesty, as a certain surgeon did when making a post-mortem on an old patient. He practically took the body apart and remarked that he could not find the soul. Such an inveterate materialist does not forget, but purposely shuts out the other ways to the discovery of the truth and facts about God, or the soul. No one living has ever seen God or a soul, but neither has anyone ever seen an electron. Has he ever seen the "power" of a chemical element? Or the composition of a split atom? Or the magnetism of a magnet? There are many things he has not seen and believes in. He has never seen his own brain, and still believes he has one. The most important things that concern man, which time and again reveal themselves to those who want to see and know, he persists in fighting and ignoring.

There are many things in this universe which cannot be produced as material facts, but which are here. Evidence of their existence comes to our reason and to our emotions the heart. We accept facts, and at the same time recognize that our emotions are very real and powerful, although they have no corporeal existence.

The soul has intelligence, and man, to express this intelligence, studies signs, words, and has experiences. Having acquired them, he uses them to express his thoughts, but that does not mean he never had thoughts before he learned anything. He could have them, as can be noticed in an infant, who tells the world when he is soiled, wet, hungry, or tired, by crying. This child comes into the world endowed with thoughts of gratification of all his needs, of the satisfaction of his hunger, of self-preservation, and of love. This state, Freud calls the Id.

With our thoughts we can build up a personality of selfish interests, evil inclinations, or a state of sanctity or humility; this is what we may call an Ego. This may not conform to Freud's Ego, because the relationship between the Id and Ego are not present here. The Id becomes incorporated with the mind after the acquisition of knowledge. The soul and its mind take over the controls.

The senses and sense organs work in two ways, with and without awareness. In plants, they work automatically. In living beings, they work either automatically alone, or in harmony with consciousness. Where thinking and thoughts are affected, the soul is concerned.

Remembering, also, is a chief part of man's intellect and life; and it is used in recalling his past joys and woes; in quarreling with his record and planning its improvement; and on his power of recollection depend all man's explaining and aspirations and learning; because all of his learning is an accumulation of memories. Among these memories, man has sensations which he analyzes and cloaks in ideals. Among the highest ideals that he possesses should be the care of his soul-life and the eventual vision of God.

The Soul and Man

WE CAN LOGICALLY ILLUSTRATE the existence of the soul by many things about us. Radio and television can give us good comparisons. Let us take television, for instance.

Everybody knows television is an electronic system for the taking of scenes, sounds, and actions, and transmitting them over the air to other sets where the visual images are reproduced. Television is wonderful, but it is mechanical. By itself, it is an entity without a soul. To be operated and worked, it must have an intelligence present from the start to the end. At the beginning, there must be an intelligence which will know what to take, and how to take it, into the camera. At the broadcasting station there must be an intelligence which will observe, manage, and regulate the receiving and the sending-out apparatuses; and at the end, at the home cabinet set, there must be an intelligence which knows how to operate the set and observe, as well as to understand, the sounds, actions, and scenes as they are reproduced on the tube and in the set.

Television represents man in the body; electric power in the system represents life; and the workers—cameramen, engineers, and others, as well as those who stay before a set, viewing and listening to everything—are all the total intelligence, or the soul.

There has to be an intelligence present at all the different stages of radio, television, and many other modern inventions, to understand them and know how to manipulate them. They could not come into existence without an intelligence interested in them. Neither could man, if he had no intelligence, or soul, as a part of him, and had not been created by God, the Great Creating and Governing Intelligence. As Pope said:

Know then thyself, presume not God to scan,
The proper study of mankind is man.

Man was not only endowed with life and soul—because there is no proof that the human organism was generated from lower animals, or that the soul is generated by human parents—with reason and the five senses; he was also given the faculties of speech, movement, digestion, elimination, sleep, and many others. He is a creature who can build up his mind and greatly alter his behavior; be subject to the most obscure emotional states and fluctuations, resulting from his many former memories; depend on others; have ideals and urgent longings for love, power, and honor; possess hidden fears and resentments. He is a consciously planning and conspiring creature.

Man may be an infinitesimal dot in an infinite universe, but he is, nevertheless, the only foundation upon which any social order can be built. He is a complex being whose complexity we call personality; the philosophic or any other system which, like religion, claims to deal with his personality must be judged by his whole personality and not by a single department of it.

A sociologist, rather than the psychologist or the philosopher, deals with the whole of man, and not merely with a selection of him. As our "rationalists" consider only parts of him, this does not make them sociologists. Man must be considered completely; he could not produce a social order, good or evil, if he possessed no soul, or innate intelligence; and you cannot build up society if you ignore his behavior, virtues, morality and immorality, etc., because they are not properties of matter, but of the spiritual world.

A cell expresses life in its functions but is not a unit of life. The structure and functions of a cell are so complex that they stagger the mind. No matter how simple, or minute, an organism —the cell—may appear, it is still an infinitely complex thing, and cannot, yes, could not, originate accidentally from simple solutions or infusions.

Man's body is composed of nearly thirty trillion cells. Each cell is an independent and separate unit of living matter, but, at the same time, a co-operating part of a larger body. Here we must pause and ask how did the cell get this co-operating influence? If the primitive cell can divide and subdivide into many cells and they do not cohere to make a mass, how can evolution explain the source and nature of this power to produce mass?

The brain is composed of some ten billion nerve cells. These and all the other different kinds of cells in the body are made of the same living matter, protoplasm. This substance takes different forms in different tissues, and in this way is able to perform some particular specialized function. Muscle cells contract, nerve cells carry impulses or messages; red blood cells carry oxygen, etc. In all the operations of the human body, these cells function co-operatively to produce effects as members of the whole organism. Why? Because there is life and a soul to bind and direct them. When life and the soul leave, their functions are dead. As in television there must be an intelligence to control and bind and direct the system, so also in the human body it is revealed that there must be an intelligence which binds and controls the cells and other parts.

How long man has been here no one knows! The Roman Catholic Church takes no definite stand on how long man has been on this earth, nor does she forbid anyone to evolve his own theories about the development of matter, so long as he believes that God created all things, or that there was a First Cause. She does expect one to believe the immediate creation of man and woman as recorded in Genesis, and that the soul of man was not produced by evolution, but directly created by the Almighty Creator. Aside from this, anyone may evolve his own theory about the age of man, so long as he keeps along the lines of good common sense and of Nature's own story.

Man was put on this globe for a purpose, and, as everything here has some specific function to perform, so also man must have a specific function. He is not here to waste his life but to live it through, with its various problems, wavering between choices of Heaven or Hell; to achieve or not to achieve his final goal, which is the Vision of God.

Concerning Man

I

MODERN MAN IS APPROXIMATELY more or less fifty thousand years old.

The construction of the material part of this man reflects the type and model of other material bodies, but it does not definitely prove that man developed from any of them. The fact that a sailing schooner can be built of wood and cloth, on the model of a sailboat, does not imply that the schooner developed from the sailboat. It was merely the model that was used to build a larger and better boat on a greater and better scale. God used the matter of the earth to make man; He could have caused the human body to evolve from some lower form of animal life up to the appropriate stage, and then He could have infused the spiritual entity, the soul, into it. Anyway, He made man the highest and best creation of His efforts.

Some rudimentary organs may have come down from some former ancestors who possessed the parts in a perfect state, but due to changed habits of life they became greatly reduced from disuse or some other cause. Some organs, as the gills and tail, could have come to us in some way from the sperm. Remember, the latter lives and swims in fluid!

That man developed from monkey is questionable and cannot be proven. There has never been found a fossilized or living ape with a human-type pelvis, and neither has any man or human fossil ever been found with an ape-type pelvis.

Man's body is only his secondary concern. His primary interest is in his spiritual entity, his soul, which is something very special, something superior to and more important than his body. But the body is wonderful also! It is a complex chemical laboratory. Chemical powers do not produce life, intelligence, wisdom, and all of the attributes of a spiritual entity. Life is not the distinctive property of complex chemical compounds. An atheist will tell you he knows what life is and will give you quite a fantastic story about it, but he is unable to produce it outside of the mere processes of life.

Man's body has a certain life span. He has just so many years. It is doubtful if any person has lived the full span allotted to him. By avoiding elements detrimental to existence, he has prolonged his stay on earth and is managing to live a little farther in his span.

All living beings, except man, have a specific, implanted brain and mind; and their thought capacity is limited to certain knowledge which is either instinctive or associated with instinct or nature. In animals, intellect and curiosity are low, besides, they are all earthbound and isolated. Man, possessing a great capacity of intellect, is not earthbound and his struggles are against isolation.

All living creatures, except man, have their own methods and forms of habitation, sustenance, reproduction, love, play, defense, and service, in their own inherent and limited ways. Man possesses all of these, but not in such a limited sense. His capacity is very great, although not endless; his endowments, in the mental state, surpass all others. His reasoning and intellectual powers are of high quality; besides, he has free emotions, magnificent discernment and power of judgment. He has imagination and can read, reason, and plan for the future. He has a sense of balance. And, in spite of all of his attributes, he is not omniscient. Where man's senses and attributes are limited, God endowed him with the acquirement of knowledge in the matter of supplementing his deficiencies by inventing artificial senses, sense organs, and other means.

A person must not forget that his mind is not like a phonograph record, which takes in without reasoning, and gives out what it has taken in. Any thoughts, ideas, or opinions coming into the mind are immediately scrutinized by our conscious self, conforming to its mental capacity, and are accepted or rejected. Our thinking processes are constantly active, whether we are awake or asleep. Our real thinking is done when any of these processes are under the control of our conscious self, the soul. Our unconscious self is the brain, which is a storehouse of thought upon which the mind of the soul acts when it is in the act of thinking.

Every person has a certain capacity to think, depending upon his education and acquisition of knowledge and experience. His convictions are the result of such knowledge. His critical thought amounts to the extent of this knowledge. If we all possessed the same amounts and limits of knowledge, we would all think almost alike, but, as this is not so, every one of us thinks in various degrees and in various ways, because of deficiencies. This state of mind is responsible for much confusion of thought in this world.

Our thoughts, opinions, and ideas are the result of reasoned consideration, whenever we absorb any of them heedlessly; sooner or later, we bring them forward and give them our critical analysis. If we are satisfied, we keep them; if not, we banish them.

Home environment has a great influence upon our mental state. Home environment surpasses general environment. It makes a better product of man if it is above the level of the general conditions and influences. When it drops to or below the level of the other, something is wrong in the home. Under general conditions and influences, man has an equal chance in evolvement. With a good background and through endeavor, he can become a better product. Those who have the means advance higher, while those who have little or none lag behind. Man's progress is the sum total of his efforts and means; not of his general environment. Man's progress creates the general environment, and not the latter, the man. The human species, no matter what its color or race, is born equal in political and spiritual rights, but not in health, wealth, capability, and home environment.

Mental theorizing about the origin of life by some learned men seems to follow a line of simplicity, or of least resistance. Their thinking is done in the manner of people thinking over a problem. They formulate a plan of what may be done and how, and everything appears to be simple. But when they tackle their problem, they come to obstacles they did not expect, or to un-anticipated matters interrelated with the problem, so that what seemed a simple and easy thing turns out to be a very complex, irritating, and tedious affair. Why? Because there were many other angles or things which did not show themselves; which were not obvious or expected, but which turned up to hamper or obviate their theoretical contention. This theorizing about the origin of life and of the processes of evolution of man is based in a similar manner on what a scientist can deduct from his observations and experiments, but of what other factors were present at that creative period he knows nothing, or simply ignores them.

I I

Matter, by itself, cannot think; it has to be manipulated by someone possessing intelligence. All products of matter have to have an intelligence responsible for their existence, be it the mind of man or the Mind of God.

Using another comparison, similar to that of television, let us compare man, in his duality, to a steam-power system. Taking the material factors of both, we have: The boiler = the stomach; engine = the heart; water = the blood; pipes = arteries, veins; machinery = the limbs; fire = the digestion; fuel = the food; heat = the nerve power; shafts, pulleys, wheels, and belts = the joints, muscles, etc.; safety gadgets = nerves and glands, and so on. Taking the spiritual factors, we have:

Fireman = the intelligence to feed and maintain.

Engineer = the brain and intelligence to control and guide.

Machine hands = the intelligence to produce.

All of these factors represent the human body and soul.

Here again, we have proof of a duality present from the time of origin, of a thing or person, until the destruction of the thing or the death of the human body. Here is another proof that an intelligence must be present and be responsible for the existence of the material thing, and that an intelligence must have been present when man was formed and endowed with a soul.

We do not come into this life born old or middle-aged, nor

do we stop at a certain age and remain there. Our bodies are born endowed with life and a soul, and go through their existence progressively from birth to old age. The soul has a God-given intelligence and other innate instincts; we acquire knowledge from without. The intelligence uses this knowledge to forward the body's pursuit of good or evil. As everything in this world is indestructible, nothing is lost, it only changes into something else or transits into space or into the unseen realm; and so it is with the soul, at death it also goes on to another world.

At the beginning of the existence of earth's creatures, life was given them by a pre-existing living being, a being of the same species. In all of this life, an observer can see a marvelous plan, the operation of wonderful laws, the exactness of design, and the intricate interplay of forces under the direction of a guiding principle. He sees in living things the work of the infinite intelligence that designed life and brought it into being. He recognizes the grandeur and majesty of the Creator, and admires the wisdom and omnipotence of God.

The central aim of life is to wed knowledge with wisdom, to enable man both to do and to do what is good. And an aim of this life also is to give each man and child his own pattern of development and his own rate of growth or decline. By this other aim of life, working in accord with certain laws of Nature, every few years we lose a great part, if not the whole, of our body; every cell has been replaced with a new cell; this and other wonderful transformations take place in each individual person; also, these changes take place in other creatures, and yet we all remain the same living beings. In other ways, it is not commonly appreciated how different we are from one another in the way we see, hear, taste, smell, and feel, nor the great differences which may arise out of the fact that each of us has distinctiveness in his or her internal glands, and the hormones they secrete. Our differences usually appear in our mental and emotional make-up. For example, man's sensual love is usually for things, while a woman's love is for persons. A man will give you excuses for his love of things but a woman will not, she just loves.

In considering man's body let us ponder a few questions: Who knew that the eye would be a delicate organ and that it needed eyelids and eyelashes to protect it? Who considered that man's vision must be evolved so that it would fit the sun's radiation? Who knew the laws of optics by which the eye was to be constructed? Could it be possible that the eye could be constructed without the knowledge of optics, or the organs of hearing without the knowledge of sound? Who knew that the ear should be built like a piano with thousands of fibers of various lengths to vibrate with the exterior sounds? And who knew what the sounds were to be? Were our ears endowed with a much greater capacity of receiving different sounds and not limited to a certain range of reception, we would not be able to hear anything because of the noise and din of the molecules in motion. We would be deafened with sound and our ears would be useless. Who understood that point when creating man?

Who knew that the eye was to see, the ear to hear, and the hand to touch, feel, and grasp? Who knew there would be variations in light and objects, both far and near, and that the eye must be built to adapt itself to them? Who knew that in all of the bones of the body there must be size, structure, and form, and that all of the details must be calculated accurately to insure suppleness and solidity, and to facilitate all of the movements necessary for their functions?

Who knew that, in the alimentary tract, food is to travel a certain way; or, in the circulatory system, that blood is to flow a certain way? Who planned the amnion, or water jacket, in which the human embryo floats, to be a shock absorber against jolts or blows which may strike the body of the mother? Who directed that bodies of men, animals, and plants had to have an outside covering to encase their organs, or processes, to produce an entity? Who thought that fruits, nuts, and vegetables had to have a covering skin or shell, so that the contents could be kept intact and preserved for shorter or longer periods of time for the food needs of man?

Of course, it was not the work of a blind atheistic evolution but the planning and creations of a Supreme Mind. This Consciousness of the universe, which endowed man with life and a tireless soul, is God, the one absolutely and infinitely perfect Spirit, who is the source of all things and who is the Creator of all.

Man and Free Will

WE, OURSELVES, MAKE MOST of our fortunes good or bad; if we do not live in a contented spirit, in Christian sobriety; if we fear to die for Christ, or to sit on our own thorns; then a calamity can sit heavily upon us. No man has blessings enough at the moment in his possessions to outweigh the evils of a great affliction. Whatever goal you have, you have a planned path to reach it, and you must keep to it to get there; and so to Heaven you have a planned path, to which you must stick or otherwise you will not reach there.

God knows all things and controls and moves them; supernatural action depends upon His Grace; but man has free will, he can co-operate or resist Grace; he is responsible for his own actions; his will, though weakened by original sin, was not destroyed; it is not a lifeless, passive thing. His free will is the faculty of making a reasonable choice among several alternatives. God knows what your choice will be and He knows you will make it freely.

Freedom of thought is liberty to think the truth and not to think as one pleases, and free will is similar to it, because man has freedom to act as he pleases within God's Commandments, but not contrary-wise. Only a mind with evil intent would object to that condition.

The object of man's will is universal goodness; the object of his mind is universal truth. These will not be found in any creatures or things of this world, but in God alone. Because God alone can satisfy man's will, hence God alone constitutes man's happiness. This man's real happiness consists in the attainment of his last end, the Vision of God. To enjoy the Vision of the Almighty, one must be immortal, and that is a value man's soul possesses.

There is in man a continual struggle between the spirit and the flesh. The body, senses, and imagination are not subject to the intellect and the will; they always want to be free, but the will can keep them in check only if it is helped by Grace and prayer.

Mind is the seat of the intellect. The will is the seat of character, choice, love, inclination, and responsibility. If there be something spiritual in man, the will must be such. If there be a will, there must be spirituality in man. The intellect, first, takes in things before it gives them out; while the will's effort is always outward. The powers of the mind and free will are rooted in a Spiritual Soul, and are served by their material organs. They are not due to evolution or some biological process, but are the creation of Someone who is free and intelligent.

Man, being a creature of free will and of untold possibilities, is not the slave of his environment; he, being the creature and creator of history, keeps on being a potential creator here, rather than the involuntary victim of his creations. He has the liberty to think the truth, but not the liberty to think as he pleases. Rational nature demands that he devote his mind to the truth, in spite of outside forces and his own appetites, although his organic appetites are subject to his will and reason.

He has free will but cannot go to extremes with it; there are rules and regulations he must follow to attain his goal, Heaven. He has no choice, because he is like the bird which must work its wings to fly, or it would fall and get killed; or like the ship which must be handled and directed, or else it would drift to destruction.

Prudence directs his free acts and is concerned with the pursuit of his moral good and the avoidance of moral evil. God endowed him with instinct, not habit, because habit is not an instinct, it is something acquired; and he lives by instinct until he becomes capable of learning to manage his life by use of his will. Instinct, then, becomes only secondary when activity is produced by power of his will.

He was not endowed with free will and intellect for nothing, and the rules of the universe do not discourage him from making use of them. Man is here to work out his salvation, but he must want to be saved. His actions have an end for themselves, and this end is a means to a greater end; this may continue until it reaches its final, or supreme, end; if it be good, it would be Heaven; if it be evil, Hell.

You cannot get inside another person to move his will; the person alone is endowed to exercise it. The evil spirit cannot impose himself upon you to do evil, it is your will power that gives in to the Devil.

Where we find human choice, we have the free act of the individual; that is, the act is the result of a person's deliberate choice. Such an act is called a moral act. Call it what you will, it still comes down to the fact that the person willed the act. Outside forces may have conditioned the act, but the person himself made the final decision.

If a person set up a limited space wherein he could put some of his pets to live and breed, he would know the limitations of that space and of its advantages to his pets. By understanding the life, habits, and other factors important to his pets, he could calculate the life span and possible existence of the animals within that limited space, in spite of the freedom of movement they have therein. When one knows the attributes and limitations of a thing, one can predict a consequence. So with man, when God placed him in this limited world. He could tell him what his probable existence would amount to, but He gave him free will within this space, so that, living according to God's precepts and commandments or not, man can shape his final happiness or doom.

Man alone has a capacity for happiness and misery. God, in His infinite mercy, does not desire his damnation.

God and Providence

He who comes from above is over all. He who is from the earth belongs to earth, and of the earth he speaks. He who comes from heaven is over all.

JOHN 3:31

I

SOME RESEARCHERS, studying life and the universe, reveal the following as some wonders of God:

1. The reflection of power in everything, from the smallest atomic particle to the largest sun.

2. The immensity of His works in the universe.

3. The complexity and variety of things, and the simplicity of all of them.

4. The law and order of Nature, revealing a wondrous Intelligence.

5. The permeation of beauty in all reality, appealing to man's emotions or spiritual sense.

6. The fundamental characteristics of all living creatures.

7. His wisdom of planning, directing, and producing, in evolutionary phases.

8. The characteristics of Nature and Providence, reflecting His attributes.

God is a property that makes the material world go. He imparts the action and motion. Matter cannot do that. A spiritual substance can. A spiritual substance, expressing itself through the body of man, is man's personality. The Personality of God, His Substance, expresses itself through His Spirit and works.

God is a Spirit; we are of that Spirit and akin to it. Spirituality is the essence of a Cosmic Consciousness, which is beyond the properties of matter, and not measurable by human mind and methods. Man's consciousness has force to govern him and his material substance. God's Consciousness has potentialities, has force and power to direct, form, drive, and make things click in the universe and in Nature's intricacies.

God, the Consciousness of the universe, is more basic than space and matter. He is not a human being and cannot be measured by a human mind. If a germ had intelligence and reason, how could it measure man? Man is an immensity compared to it. The universe seems an immensity to man, but not to God, who, being of cosmic extent, can look down upon man as the latter looks down upon the germ.

God is the life and the power of motility, which permeates the universe as a major cosmic influence. The Creator is not only the Lord of the earth, He is the Master of the universe. If there be living beings on any other planets, God will see that they are subject to Him. He will mete out to them His Providence, and will reward good and punish evil.

Though the existence of life on other planets is merely a conjecture, the Bible tells us that all life, everywhere, is subject to Him. "And will gather His elect . . . from the uttermost parts of the earth to the uttermost parts of heaven" (Mark 13:27). Also the Scriptures tell us that God in His house has many mansions.

Man is born of this earth and his offspring are all bound to this earth. Their responsibilities to God will not be removed even if they try to move off this globe to set up a new home on another planet. No matter where in the universe a man may settle, if it becomes possible, evil will not be condoned by God, while good will always find His approval and reward.

What the Almighty has placed upon the other planets is His affair; we will never be able to have any personal contact with life thereon, if such exists. Building up hypotheses about existence there from appearances and composing a halo of factuality about these theories is deceitful. Our existence is concerned with this earth and everything within reach of it, and not worlds and galaxies at inaccessible distances. There is no living man within thousands of millions of light years of travel from our globe.

Even our close planets are questionable. On Mars, for instance, life seems possible. But there is nothing promising there. The green patches which have been seen there by some astronomers may not be plant life; in fact, some contend that there are no green patches, instead, the color is gray and this gray reveals only deposits of lava.

Matter, energy, time, and space are our four basic entities. There is a fifth entity, a superentity which is more basic, unlike, and indispensable than the other four, but which embraces them all. This entity is our God.

It is not to be denied that we cannot supplant Him and His Omnipotence with the knowledge we garner from test tubes, the radio telescope, the electron microscope, the extended radiation spectrum, cosmotrons, experimental agriculture, and from mathematical equations. These are only revelations of matter in its many processes, forms, and actions.

To every "what" there is a "how" and a "why." There being a "why" always reveals a purpose; every purpose, as everyone knows, reveals a reason. Every reason reveals a mind, and that reveals an intelligence, plus a personality. In matters of life, the world, and the universe, it is the wonderful Intelligence, a Personal God. This planet and everything within it and about it, were built for the existence of life. This was set here for man, and he was set here by the Almighty for the purposes which He had revealed by Himself, through His Son Jesus Christ, and through His other agencies, be they scriptures, men, miracles, or phenomena. Many of these revelations we can find in the Bible, which remains a great source of the historical events in which the Lord revealed Himself and His purposes, by acts and deeds.

II

In our affairs, we may come to a certain point where the ways divide into many alternatives. Providence directs us into the proper channel for the best outcome. Here, we may say, a thing happened by chance or accident, but it was not such;

the favorable circumstance occurred because of the act of God, Providence. This reality, which we may call destiny or fate, is really Providence, which is here imposing itself upon us.

Such chances or accidents are not accidental, but coincidences planned and intended to achieve the unforeseen purpose of Providence; and everything happens according to some law and order, imposed by the Supreme Guiding Spirit. As the laws of Nature are not rigid in all of their work, everything does not happen in the same manner.

God, in His Providence, works without disturbing the course of natural laws and natural causality, but at the same time keeps everything under full control of His Divine Will. His freedom of action and His Providence are interrelated. Providence makes itself manifest in single and in multiple events, but none of these can be studied in the sense of probabilities which will happen again. There is no dealing here with matter or material phenomena. Chance does not apply to any real happenings; it cannot be a course of events; nor is there any property inherent in it. When a large number of repeated events happen in specified time, they actualize themselves. Upon such a basis science also rests.

Tossing a coin into the air to see what the result will be when it falls down upon a surface is usually considered in the category of chance; but, if the conditions were known through which the coin goes from the start of the toss to its falling and settling upon a surface, it could be possible to predict the outcome of the toss, thus separating chance from reality. If all of the influences and stimuli the First Cause used in producing the first living organism were known, the words "fortuitous," "hazard," and "chance" would not be resorted to.

This sense of reality has to be completely determined, while chance, accident, and probability should have no place in it. Their existence in the universe is undeniable, but they did not exist in the creative moment of the historic past, in the planned purpose of creating life without a First Cause.

When it comes to phenomena which may occur outside the natural laws, it will be found that most such phenomena occur in situations where they cannot be available for study, or be put to the application of science. Because of such limitations, it is absurd to claim that nothing happened when something really did occur. Many such occasions can be classified in the category of chance.

God gave Nature the laws for all existence. He has His own laws, which He can interpose between the natural laws whenever He wishes. He is not obligated to mere man to reveal all of His handiwork and methods. He has His own trade secrets, which He will not reveal to man (Mark 8:11-12). The Creator gave the universe its form, composition, and the laws according to which He wants it to operate. He does little to hinder or disturb any of these laws when He interposes between them. We also have instances outside of God's intervention, where natural laws interpose between themselves. In the historic past, the Creator set the universe, and He wants it to operate according to the laws He endowed it with and according to His plans. His principal concern is man and man's soul, which are the main objects of His providential care, justice, mercy, and salvation. The other interests of Providence are man's world affairs and his private life. Scripture tells us that we are worth more to Him than the birds and the flowers.

III

Atheism is of two kinds—speculative and practical. There is no reasonable basis for speculative atheism, nor any moral basis for practical atheism. Neither form holds out anything to man but the destruction of all personal life. But for him who does not close his eyes to the light and who knows how to observe and read in Nature the manifestations of a creative wisdom, to him the existence of an all-wise Personal God is revealed, and the assurances of a future life which will realize his fullest aspirations; he will understand that the continual intervention of Providence, attentive to the necessities of the least of creatures, will encourage him in the struggles and difficulties of his daily life, and in the accomplishment of his duties, and will implant in his soul the hope of attaining someday the Beatific Vision.

Every living organism, at its origin, begins with a cell. This cell divides and multiplies itself, and, without exception, it could go on producing itself in the same type of cell. What is the supernatural agency, power, or force that knows how to gather and form from these cells organisms differing widely from each other, according to their varied species? Surely, the intervention of a supernatural agency is evident here, as well as in the natural course of all events of man and Nature. Testimony to the evidence is given unceasingly and in many forms.

An egg will produce a beast, bird, or fish, but its evolutive property is not a product of physics or chemistry, nor can it be explained by the mechanical forces of atoms. We must, of necessity, recognize a directive principle which guides the evolution of living organisms, and this directive principle is resident only in an intelligence.

It is evident that those things, which are attributed to the works of Nature, are not produced by, or dependent on, the will of men. There is, therefore, some other Spirit that causes them, since they cannot subsist of themselves.

If we diligently consider the constant regularity, order, and linking together of natural things, the surprising magnificence, beauty, and perfection of the larger, and the exquisite contrivance of the smaller parts, together with the exact harmony and correspondence of the whole, and at the same time attend to the import of the attributes, one eternal, infinitely wise, good, and perfect, we shall clearly perceive that they belong to a Spirit, God, who works all in all, and in whom all things exist.

There is widespread human testimony concerning the existence of a Supreme Being, although different opinions are given regarding His nature and attributes. In fact, it would be very difficult to explain this testimony, if a Supreme Being did not exist. His detailed and momentary care for everything in this world, and the complete dependence of everything and every person in the world upon Him, is always evident.

When men say that Nature aspires to progress and perfection, they allude to Providence; because there is no such thing as an aspiring Nature. By Nature, we mean only the sort, the kind, the species, or the class of a thing; because there is a difference between the words "nature" and "Nature." The former indicates a characteristic or a property of matter; the other means the works of God, or of His Providence. It is hypocrisy to deny Providence, and ascribe to "Nature" such supernatural powers evident in the nature of things. Providence is the action of an all-wise God, manifest in the material order; it was known in ancient biblical times; and today it can be reconciled to scientific causality; the attempt is not impossible.

If there were not an attentive and guiding force, everything in this universe, in time, would come to the point of equilibrium, inertia, and stagnation. God does not desire that, so His Providence keeps everything in motion. He will know when to end it all.

The Almighty, in His Providence, has given man liberty to choose his mode of living, which the animal cannot do. Man can prepare his food artificially, or make clothes, which the animal cannot.

To realize God's care, we need only to view casually the intricate incomprehensibility of bodily perfection to become astounded. An amazing example is the realization that less than two thousandths of an ounce of a chemical called thyroxine is all that lies between the cleverest human being and blank imbecility.

Provision for all living is revealed in phenomena which we know today, but which Darwin did not know—such as the wonders of genes. And, by the economy of Nature, we are forced to realize that only infinite wisdom could have foreseen and made preparation with such wise husbandry. Checks and balances have been universally provided. What is the controlling power that governs the height of man, or of a plant; so that each has its growth limitations to its certain species? Genes give us the characteristics, but what force knows when the tree has reached its height's limit? Think of the development of a child to manhood; how great the progress during those years. Think of the development of any living organism. What controls this development, or evolution? Surely, it is not atheistic evolution.

When winter approaches, how do the birds know it is warm in the southern countries and fly there? Who instructs them in the building of their nests? Of course, it is nothing else but God and His Providence. He overlooks nothing and no one. Grass is killed so that cattle can be nourished; and the cattle die so that man can live. Men die because their stay here is temporary, or transitional; they must appear before their God for disposal. Everything is a part of the wisdom of God and the works of His Providence.

IV

Have you seen God? Have you seen electricity? No, but electricity has revealed itself to you in many ways, and so you believe it exists. God has been revealing Himself, also, in countless ways, and still you will not believe in Him. Is there not some contrariness in your life's pattern? If you could harness God and make Him serve you; if you could find means to dominate your Creator, you would feel much better off. Since you are subject to Him, it is not to your liking; you would prefer He did not exist. Your inferiority complex irritates you; ignoring God bolsters your ego. That is no help; He is still by you and watches your every action, and there will come a moment when the whole reality of life will come before you, but it may be too late! History fails to teach man!

Do not put your entire faith in science to reveal everything, because beyond the bounds of Nature, science is no better off than you; it can only doubt or believe on faith. It is puzzling by what logic a bit of gray matter in a thick skull, no larger than a melon, dares think God does not exist, or cannot do things. When will man learn not to measure the Almighty by the finite smallness of his own mind? Job saw, thousands of years ago, the futility of finite man's reasoning in attempting to define God.

When a person gets to prying, he gets himself into trouble. It is none of his concern what God is, or does. A servant does not question his master! The Supreme Being reveals Himself in many ways, unceasingly, so that man can notice Him and believe. Why not do it now?

In the numerous acts of Providence we see the Hand of God. When the lemmings propagate rapidly, becoming a destructive nuisance, Providence causes them to mass migrate at irregular intervals of several years, and myriads of them plunge into the sea and perish. We observe that marine life, as well as plant life, whichever has its existence jeopardized by its environment, is endowed providentially with an astonishing fecundity, so that its species will not be exterminated.

Animals, unlike plants, are not fixed to the soil; they move about and seek their food. Whose vision was it, if not God's, that they have need of senses capable of seeing the objects necessary for their existence; of organs of locomotion and of apprehension, in order to obtain food?

In every man's life are there not occurrences of escapes, dangers, and bits of chance, which, when well examined, prove that the Hand of God has worked in them? Is the fact that the temperature of the earth has been fitted for life for uncounted millions of years, while outlying regions of space are unlivably hot or cold, not one of the works of Providence? There are innumerable cases that can be cited as evidence of the Supreme Being's existence, through His providential deeds.

There are other examples of God's patience running out with the evils of man. Then He deals out drastic punishment. Though some horrors may be attributed to natural or geologic origin, others were surely "acts of God" or "acts of Providence," because every one had an authentic evil history preceding its disaster.

The Hand of the Almighty took revenge when times were exceedingly sinful and evil, as in biblical days there were: the Great Flood; the Confusion of Tongues at Babel; the Destruction of Sodom and Gomorrah; the Destruction of Jerusalem; and in more recent ages, in the horrible fire in a Paris charity bazaar in 1897; the San Francisco earthquake and fire; the Chicago fire; the sinking of the pirates' lair, the city of Port Royal, Jamaica, in 1692; the destruction of St. Pierre, in Martinique, by Mount Pelée in 1902; etc.

In all of these places of horror, man had tried the patience of God with evil doings. This is a matter of fact and not imaginary legend. When or where the "act of God" shows its might, you will not find a person who believes in the Lord and who knows the consequences, who will deny it was His work. It is always the materialists who try to deny Him and His actions, and make all efforts to minimize that knowledge or prevent its dissemination.

Investigating St. Pierre, in Martinique, F.W.I., for instance; things were revealed in very bad shape. Subtracting a few people from the forty thousand population, the remainder were all Communistic materialists or sympathizers. On the day of destruction, a blasphemous celebration was to have been held. Christ and religion were to be mocked and ridiculed. God, in His mercy, tried to warn the sinful people of their threatened doom, by the behavior of the volcano, Mount Pelée. A small number of the Lord's faithful escaped, the previous day, to the neighboring hills, to save their lives from the possible eruption and from the wrath of the mobs. On the day of the celebration, in May, 1902, the mountain erupted and destroyed the city with all of its inhabitants, except one, who was a prisoner in the jail. As the rainbow appeared after the Great Flood, in remembrance of the great catastrophe, a Bishop's Ring, a reddish-brown corona around the sun, followed the death of St. Pierre.

We must recognize God's deeds in this world, be they manifest in whatever form. We must be humble and submissive. Absolute independence would destroy both us and our freedom.

God and Faith

THE SEEKER OF GOD sees the Almighty as the famous Swedish botanist, Linnaeus, the author of a remarkable classification of botany did, when he wrote: "The eternal God, immense, allwise and omnipotent, has left His seal on the creation of His hands. My soul has seen the reflection of the Almighty in His creatures, and I have been plunged in a stupor of admiration.

I have followed here and there His traces in the things of Nature, and seen His work even in the most diminutive and imperceptible of beings; what power, what wisdom, what ineffable perfection! I have seen how the world of animated beings is linked to the vegetable kingdom, and how this again is connected with the mineral kingdom. . . . The sun and the whole sidereal system, immense, incalculable, appear to me suspended by the hand of that Prime Motor, the Cause of causes, the guide and preserver of the universe. All created things bear testimony to that unfathomable wisdom and power divine; their beauty, their harmony, and their just proportions, proclaim the omnipotence of that great God."

As Linnaeus saw God in everything, so can anyone who wants to. A man does not need to resort to science to deduce what the Almighty is, because science is limited, and God does not fall within the province of any natural science. God is the author of both true science and true religion.

By reason, man knows things; by faith, he believes things. By reason, man can have a realization of God's existence, some of His attributes, and even the existence of revelation; but, by reason alone, he is deficient in the knowledge of the intrinsic mysteries revealed by the Great Mind, because to know these things, revelation and faith are necessary. Man believes them because God revealed them. Faith perfects reason; it does not contradict reason, because faith is concerned not with knowledge opposed to reason, but with knowledge above reason.

A person does not see his brain or heart, but believes he possesses them, because he was told by someone who had not seen his own, but had also been informed by someone else, who possibly, though he had not seen his own, had been told by someone who has seen someone else's, and thereby believes that every man has a brain and a heart. That is faith.

In research, the scientist has a motive; this motive is a mystery; he visualizes it and plans his efforts to attain it. A person with faith has a motive; this motive is a mystery; he visualizes it and plans his efforts to attain it also.

To believe, man has faith; to believe, it is not necessary to know. There is a difference between the word "believe" and the word "know." The word "believe" states that the person has faith and an accepted opinion, be it factual or not; the word "know" reveals the person has factual knowledge.

God endowed man not only with instinct, the organs of sense, intelligence, etc., but also with conscience. Man is gifted with intelligence that he may recognize, in contradistinction to the animals; have connection with God, His goodness and love; and enter in filial relation with Him; have faith in Him and lead a higher life.

Man's intelligence constitutes his highest excellence. In the past, he used his intelligence mostly for the purpose of separating himself from his Creator; in his early days he refused to listen to his Master, originated sin, and followed the inspiration of his reason. Through the centuries, he wished to be a teacher and lawgiver, and made of himself "the little god of the earth." He builds on his errors, and is followed by disaster.

Even today, many refuse to believe, in spite of all the evidence plainly seen, because they know that if their wills accepted what their reason admits to be true, they would have to give up a lot of bad living, which they hate to do.

The knowledge of the existence of the Creator and the high destiny of man comes not only from God's revelations of Himself, and of man's relation to Him, but also from the faculty of reason, from the consensus of correctly formed opinion, and from man's faith, and his hope for complete happiness.

Some people do not believe because they have knowingly and deliberately failed to inform themselves properly on matters of religion. Most of them seem to be well informed in other matters, but lacking in faith; they have a culpable unbelief; that is, they choose not to believe and refuse to study a faith; a faith which is an acceptance of truth on the authority of God. Though the truth may be beyond reason, it is not contrary to reason.

To a person who does not have faith religion seems an absurdity, and it makes him feel ridiculous or out of place. This non-conformist relaxes into a self-contained earthly paradise, the paths of which head straight for the gates of Hell. For the one who has religion, it is the happy answer to all of his desires. It is not a blaze of sentiment, nor is he a plaything of his passions. It concerns his entire being, what is best in it, that is, his soul. His faith is an interior movement of his whole being, including that of his intellect and will. He is so created that he can lose or save his own soul, and his religion tells him the results of his efforts.

The concept of an idea of God reveals there must be an Almighty Master of the universe existing because we know that an idea is not born of itself. It must have a background, one or more premises, conditions, effects, etc., with which it is associated, and because of which it is produced. Also, every condition, effect, activity, etc., is not born of itself; it is due to pre-existing agents or causes. So, if there is an idea of God, there must be a something to cause that idea, to give us our faith in the existence of the Creator. Our faith and emotions are exercised through these conditions and influences. All of these states reveal there is a spiritual world with spiritual entities and influences, and we believe in that.

Religion

THE SECRET OF A HAPPY LIFE and an unencumbered mind is to have faith, and to lead a sincere life; not to attempt to reach the height of understanding, or to dive deep into the mysteries of God. If you believe in Him and His power, why upset yourself with curious and unprofitable searching? If you do not understand those things that are under or about you, how should you understand those things that are above you?

The study of God in His universe and in religion is an intense undertaking. You cannot expect to have anyone try to teach and explain all to you in just a few minutes. It takes years of effort and learning to master much of the needed systematic knowledge, and still this may not be sufficient, as the study seems to be endless. If you are fair-minded and have intelligence, you understand you cannot approach an engineer, doctor, lawyer, carpenter, or any other trained man, and demand that he teach you all about his profession or trade within a few minutes. A man has spent years in schooling himself to learn his art, or livelihood, and you would demand immediate knowledge of his work? You would look very ridiculous, indeed!

And still, such is the practice of many persons when it comes to the subject of God or religion. Their human reason is weak, and in most cases conceals deceit. There is something wrong in their mental make-up and attitude. From experience, it has been found that many of these questioners have a very small understanding of religion, and upon this very limited base have made their own religious opinions or ideas of God, and of their faith. They do not desire to make much effort to understand the truth, the real truth, for fear it would in some way jeopardize them or their sinful living. They fear the truth, because it limits freedom of belief, as right and moral law limit freedom of action. There is an obligation binding them, as well as every intelligent creature, to believe the truth and to do right. Because whoever gives only lip service to the teachings of faith is no more Christian than a pagan. In fact, God did not give us free will to devise our own creeds and religious systems. Adam and Eve lost their abode in the Garden of Eden for not behaving as instructed. And all freethinkers who refuse to have faith are liable to condemnation.

There is little joy or satisfaction in being a freethinker, a fringist, or an indifferent church member. Spending one's life in an awful dull and hateful mediocrity becomes depressing, not only to the mediocre themselves, but to those living in the midst of mediocrity.

The Bible admonishes us: "Be not thou anxious, nor dispute with thy thoughts, nor answer the doubts which the devil suggests; but believe the words of God, believe His Saints and Prophets, and the wicked enemy will fly from thee" (James 4:7).

It is not science that creates happiness, but a single branch of knowledge—the knowledge of good and evil. And an understanding of good and evil is impossible without a lofty sense of the meaning of life. This lofty sense is achieved only through combining an understanding of Nature with an appreciation of God. He never promised us happiness in this life as a reward for the good we do. What rewards we earn will be paid in the hereafter.

Among the rewards of souls in Heaven will be a full knowledge of the teachings of Christ, or the mysteries of our religion. Full knowledge, in this instance, means such knowledge as a human mind can grasp. A perfect knowledge is impossible; it would make us like unto God, Himself.

Faith also makes us conscious of moral obligations. These are impossible without law, and law is impossible without a lawgiver. This makes us conscious that the Supreme Lawgiver, who embodied His Law in the very nature of things, is no one else but Almighty God.

The forces of evil have tried unceasingly, through the ages, in various ways, either by force or ideology, to destroy God, Christ, and His Church, but have not succeeded. Why do they persist in their cunning ways, using every possible means to attain their ends? It is because the Church has so many fringists, who are self-centered, whose interests in the Church are last; who live on their stomachs and luxuries, and not by their soul's welfare, and who do not concentrate and make their daily efforts of value to their religion, and an obstruction to evildoers.

Primitive man, though endowed with reason, walked in a state of mental uncertainty on such vital matters as the existence of a Personal God, His creation, the immortality of the soul, the resurrection of the body, and the objective reality of Heaven and Hell. God, through Christ, revealed all to man, and filled his need of certitude.

As man was made for God, to serve and love Him, only believers can give Him the fullest measure of service and love. Love is a mental state that can be expressed physically and depends upon individual ability. True love comes from the soul, and it implies respect. Love coming from the senses does not appeal to God, and it does not make persons masters of this sensual kind of love, but rather its victims.

A man in love would turn the world upside down for his love object; he would pull down the stars from the sky, lay the moon down before his object of love; he would make the ground she walks on turn to gold, if it were possible. Do you ever feel that kind of love for your Creator? And you say you love God? Then, what is holding you back from expressing that kind of love, or something similar to it? Self-love? Your earthly affairs and temporary existence here are more important than that?

Religion and the Church

WHEN A MAN BYPASSES GOD and the spiritual world in his observations, his contention is that the continuity in the series of vital organisms on earth have emerged from inorganic molecules of the archaeozoic ooze, and have evolved to higher types of man; that man has risen from the "hot thin soup," from which also have come our bluebirds and roses. In his contention he denies Nature an end and design. He overlooks the fact that those processes of evolution were orderly and the effects intended. He tries to ignore an intelligent cause, God, which knew those effects and ends beforehand and what they would produce. There was order in those happenings, and order exacts an intelligent cause, a Mind, which was nothing else but of God.

Everything was created to exist within its own sphere of existence; because of the environment and life demands of the various creatures, man's sense organs are excelled by the corresponding receptors of many other animals. They were endowed not for favoritism, but for their own necessity. All so-called rudimentary phases or things found in the developing stages of an unborn human being, or found in our bodies after birth, are not there because an ancestor may have been a fish or some other organism, but because somewhere a certain stage of development possibly necessitated that condition or those things.

A great planning intellect is revealed in the ensemble of all creatures, and in all the processes of evolution. God-loving people can see the Almighty's work, and thereby obtain a knowledge of their Creator; in fact, this knowledge of God lies buried deep in every man and is brought forth by the study of the nature of things about him. The works of wonder wrought by God enhance man's faith and religion.

Our Creator has told us through His Son, Jesus Christ, that we are born to know, love, and serve God in this world; that our immortal souls are supernatural, and are destined for eternity in Heaven or Hell, depending on how we live. Because we believe in our Heavenly Father and in His Son Jesus, as our God, who is Almighty and All-Wise, we believe in everything He has revealed to us. We believe all, no matter what it is, because we have faith in Him and know nothing is impossible for Him. There is no place for the smallest iota of a doubt. Believing otherwise is hypocrisy, and an insult to Him who governs the world and whose word is the truth. The least doubt would deny His Divinity.

It is through the writings of the Apostles that we know Christ. Many persons claim to believe in Christ, but do not believe fully in the writings of the Apostles. They claim the Apostles exaggerated, were too given to imagination, and wrote things that seem to have no foundation. In other words, they call the Apostles liars, and then say they believe in the product (Christ) of their writings. Any sense in such assertions? Would you believe anything of anyone if you considered him a liar? There is nothing else here but ignorance, evasion, or prejudice.

Throughout the times of the Old Testament era, for centuries before Christ, His coming, suffering, and death were being revealed by the Holy Spirit, in words of prophetic fervor. The words were audaciously direct, and their meaning unmistakenly clear; there is no error in them as they are brought forth by the Scriptures. If in the biblical text there should be found any suspicion of error, a condition that would be a rarity, it would be possible that the copyist made a mistake, or the translator did not express the meaning correctly, or possibly that the reader does not understand; but there can be no error by the original writer or in the truths he portrays. This we believe when we put our faith in the Scriptures. To be a Christian, one must believe the religious truths written in them.

Whatever messages one can derive from the Bible or its concern with past history, those messages are intended only for the members of the Church which Christ established, and to the unbeliever whom Christ wants to join His Church. Christ set up one Church, and no messages from the Bible intend that His Church be disrupted and done away with, and replaced by a man-made one. Christ established one Church, which was to be universal. He commanded His Apostles: "Go ye into the whole world and preach the Gospel to every creature" (Mark 16:15). He ordered them to teach all nations (Matt. 28:19-20), and said that "whosoever will despise them will despise and dishonor Him and God, the Father" (Luke 10:16).

Christ did not build His Church for just a day or a year, but to last to the end of time, when He said: "And behold I am with you all days even to the consummation of the world" (Matt. 28:20). This organization was to last, and all of its precepts, laws, regulations, and powers were to last until the *end*. If His Church does not exist today, then He was not a God but an impostor, and all Christianity becomes a fake!

The Church is the one body where order can exist. Because where people knit loosely and are discontented; where opinions are differentiated; such a Church divides and subdivides and minces itself to small pieces. The Protestant Church is a good example of this.

Protestant Reformation was a product of man's conflict between his creed and his mode of living. He proceeded to whittle down religious truths and change the meanings and the composition of the Bible, so that they would fit his own ideas of life, and so that his conscience might be better satisfied. Others followed and continued this practice of misinterpreting the Holy Writ, so that today Protestantism has disintegrated into numerous sects, and into some forms of glamorous paganism. Besides, one can find much bigotry and Communistic infiltration of its pulpits and offices of higher rank. Even today, some Protestant seminaries do not prepare many of their men to be ministers of their acknowledged faith, but to be hypocrites and disciples of God-hating Communism and of falsehood.

The Catholic Church is against private interpretation of the Bible; is against all fake and contradictory doctrines, but is not against those who adhere sincerely to their erroneous religions and are in good faith.

Christ and the Apostles passed down to us warnings against the Anti-Christs and all false prophets. And these warnings have been repeated and repeated throughout the years, for more than nineteen centuries, but have the people harkened to them? No! Because the man whose knowledge of his religion has become weak and rusty is an easy prey of God's enemies, be they atheists, Communists, or the like. And the growth of evils today confirms this.

The Church of Christ

God never meant that man should scale the heavens
By strides of human wisdom. In His works,
Though wondrous, He commands us in His word
To seek Him rather where His mercy shines.

COOPER

I

IF WE TAKE UP THE BIBLE, we will find many references to the origin of the Church of Christ. Here are a few:

"And I say to thee, thou art Peter, and upon this rock I will build my Church, and the gates of Hell shall not prevail against it" (Matt. 16:18).

"All power in heaven and on earth has been given me. Go therefore, and make disciples of all nations, baptizing them in the name of the Father, and of the Son, and of the Holy Spirit, teaching them to observe all that I have commanded you; and behold, I am with you all days, even unto the consummation of the world" (Matt. 28:18-20).

"And he said to them, Go into the whole world and preach the gospel to every creature. He who believes and is baptized shall be saved, but he who does not shall be condemned" (Mark 16:15-16).

"Go, Behold, I send you forth as lambs in the midst of wolves" (Luke 10:3).

"He who hears you, hears me; and he who rejects you, rejects me; and he who rejects me, rejects him who sent me" (Luke 10:16).

"He therefore said to them again, Peace be to you! As the Father has sent me, I also send you" (John 20:21).

"Even as thou hast sent me into the world, so I also have sent them into the world" (John 17:18).

"But you shall receive power when the Holy Spirit comes to you, and you shall be witnesses for me in Jerusalem and in all Judea and Samaria and even to the very ends of the earth" (Acts 1:8).

"And I send forth upon you the promise of my Father. But wait here in the city, until you are clothed with power from on high" (Luke 24:49).

These few references taken from the New Testament prove that Christ established His own Church on this earth, and, being God, He promised to be with His Church to the end of the world. Besides, He promised that, while the Church exists, evil will not overpower it. If His Church does not exist today, or went astray, then it is futile to believe in any church. Christ, Himself, would be an impostor and a fraud. But that is an impossibility! Denying the existence of Christ's Church would be denying Christ as God; it would be denying His Almighty Power and making all of His statements falsehoods, and all of His miracles, fakes. And such a condition of hypocrisy exists today!

Christ established His Church and conferred upon it the jurisdiction and the power to teach all mankind. When Peter the Apostle was made the Rock of the Church, and given the keys of the Kingdom of Heaven, he was given the power to legislate, administer, and to judge. When told to "Feed my lambs, feed my sheep" (John 21:15-17), he was empowered to look after the members of the Church of Christ.

The Catholic Church was and is the Church Our Lord founded, and He endowed it with immunity from error in faith and morals. He has revealed our religion to us, and because we believe in Him to be God, present in a human body, we have faith in the revelations and traditions handed down to us by His successors and followers.

If one religion is as good as another, there would have been no necessity for Christ to come and establish His own. Any one of the religions then existing should have been good enough. To regard one religion as good as another is to affirm that God condones right and wrong, as well as truth and falsehood. The Roman Catholic Church is the only church set up by Christ, headed by Peter, and governed by his successors, the Popes, throughout the ages. There were many competitive ships which sailed the Lake of Gennesaret; but only one, that piloted by Peter, was distinguished by the presence of Christ.

The Catholic Church has been assailed and assaulted by evil men during its existence, but the forces of evil have not destroyed her. As Christ was tempted by the Devil, the Church's leaders and faithful could have been tempted to do wrong, but the Church and its teachings, passed down from its Founder, have withstood all the onslaughts of the "gates of Hell."

The Church does not invent new doctrines, she only interprets those divinely revealed. She speaks in the name of God and with Divine authority. In obeying her, the member is obeying God Himself. A Catholic does not give blind obedience to a fallible human authority that might ask him to believe what is preposterous, or subject him to a spiritual despotism. He gives obedience to a Church endowed by God with infallible Divine authority on matters of faith or morals.

The philosopher René Descartes says that often there is less perfection in works which are composite than in those which issue from a single hand. This is very certain, that the estate of true religion, which God alone has ordained, must be incomparably better guided than any other. God, through His Son, Jesus Christ, established a definite religious organization, the Church, which for the past ages has been the exponent and custodian of His teachings. He certainly cannot be pleased with those religions founded by mere man, or with their efforts to undermine and destroy His handiwork.

The Catholic Church is one, and has been the same, in its doctrines and teachings from the time of its origin; it is not like others who are split or one-sided, as part liberal or part conservative.

Religion pervades every activity of man. The Catholic Church must not allow itself and its clergy to be curtailed in all activities that are in the interests of, or affect the same, its members; and be confined only to activities inside the church building and its pulpit. Religion goes with everything in life; it cannot be separated, and neither can the Church be separated from the world and its affairs.

I I

On the first Pentecost, Apostle Peter was the first to launch out and preach to the people. Three thousand persons were baptized that first day. It was the birthday of the Catholic Church. It was the day when the Apostles "were all filled with the Holy Ghost, and they began to speak with divers tongues" (Acts 2:4).

From that day the Apostles carried on their work against all odds to spread the Gospel upon earth. After them, others followed through the ages, all inflamed by the Holy Spirit, and these were backed up by men and women as upholders of the faith, and as martyrs, who had rather suffer and die than disown the religion that was in them; and by others who sacrificed their lives to work in God's service in various capacities.

Some of our prejudiced enemies say the Church has become

old-fashioned and out of date; that we need something more progressive, more in conformity with the times. Such a statement shows they are either ignorant of the religion they attack, or are trying to undermine the Church, by playing on the fringists and weak members. Man has breathed the air surrounding him for thousands of years, and it has not become old-fashioned and out of date; as air is not here today and gone tomorrow, but is a permanent property of the earth, so is the Church not a fluctuating entity, but a permanent, basically unchanging marvel. And as it is, it will be until the end of time.

From the first century up to the present time, the Church has been basically the same. It has endeavored to convert pagans and savages to Christianity. From the first century, the work of humanizing and civilizing has been going on. There has never been a period when the Church was complete within the domains of the earth, and had no more converts to seek. Its work against paganism and superstition was, and is, unceasing. Human inclination, in spite of repeated instructions and admonitions, has been to hold fast to former superstitions or pagan practices. In some cases, the zeal, primarily for patriotism and secondarily for the Church, went so far as to produce inquisitions in certain lands where political and national aspirations predominated. The enemies of our religion seized upon these happenings and accused the Church of being responsible for them, and not those who were really responsible.

After the Reformation, the same thing happened in all of the Protestant-dominated countries, but their churches were truly closely allied with the persecutors and the persecution of our faithful.

The Spanish Inquisition was not as bad as some of its strongest critics claim. Most of the accounts are based upon the manufactured information of a renegade priest named Juan Antonio Llorente, who destroyed the original documents which he stole, and made up false tales upon which our opponents base their accusations.

Against our religion and Church, each age stirred up its traitors, its theories, and its onslaughts. Also, for our religion and

Church, each age produced its martyrs, its heroes, and its exploits. And through all of this, the Church, an ageless institution, steadfastly persevered.

The claim that the Church was a state in the Middle Ages is not true. There were countries which were predominantly Catholic, and they were ruled by Catholics, under laws of their own making. Secular authority under princes, dukes, nobles, and others, held sway in their circumscribed domains. Since each had to make terms with his environment, and so far as he might to his own advantage control it, his ways and means of enforcing laws were of incalculable importance to him, and his errors were, and are, in many instances, imputed to the Catholic Church.

Some of these states were like "family domains," ruled for the interest of its members and for attacks upon other "family domains."

There have been and are evils among Christians. These cannot be ascribed to practical Catholics. A practicing religionist stands on solid ground with his faith. His mind is not wobbly and uncertain. The ridiculous religious practices held by others cannot be thrown at him or his religion. Atheists dig up many absurd doings by non-Catholics, and accuse the Roman Church, and all religions in general, of them. They believe that by attacking all religions and churches, by accusing them in general for the malpractice of one group or sect, they gain in poisoning the minds of those who lack the "know" of their faith, because of ignorance.

The Church endeavors to remove ignorance by having all of her children educated properly; she strives to set up schools, colleges, and universities to educate her members for a proper civilization. She tries to eliminate ignorance and superstition, because the two go together. She knows an educated person is a benefit to his Church and religion.

In every century there were enemies who took advantage of the wrongdoings of a local action in some country and held the Catholic Church and religion responsible. Today, similarly, atheists in the United States use the constitutions and the laws of the federal and state governments for their own benefit and to injure those who believe in God or religion. The spirit of the American Constitution was founded on religious principles; on the recognition of a Creator, and not in the spirit of atheism, materialism, or Communism.

Another cause of confusion in religious matters in this world is the practice of private interpretation of the Scriptures. This practice has produced such a conflicting variety of opinions as to cause religious chaos and anarchy. Controversies over meanings of biblical text should be referred to the original Bible. The King James Version has been adulterated and misinterpreted. If the Confederate States of America were freed and adopted the Declaration of Independence, the Constitution, and the Bill of Rights, they would not have taken them in their original forms, but would have changed and modified their contents to their advantage. So if anyone had to do research on the origin of our laws and rights, he would not actually refer to these for his information, but would go to the originals held by the Northern states, the Union. So, likewise, it is with the Bible. The original was produced by the Catholic Church and is still in her possession. To prevent confusion, that Bible should be studied and in the manner the Roman Church prescribes. The Protestant Bible is false and erratic in interpretations; but anyway, any Bible would be confusing to the untrained mind. An authority should do the interpreting.

Persons may interpret the Scriptures and religious dogmas erroneously, and thereby interfere with the advance of knowledge. It is not the fault of the Church or religion when someone reacts mistakenly, because of his wrong sense of a religious meaning. His idea of religion is not a matter between God and himself. The Heavenly Father gave us rules and sent His Only Son to set up His organization, the Church. Being a member of that organization, a person is bound to obey and live up to its rules and regulations. God will ignore the ideas, rules, and dogmas of faith made by others whose purpose is to dodge His organization. He said so in the Bible!

Religion is based on its Scriptures, dogmas, traditions, and revelations, and not on the personal opinions of any of its adherents or of outsiders. Many errors and wrong actions have been and are attributed to the Church or religion through such opinions or activities.

In matters concerning spirit and religious obligations, there cannot be any assertions and findings made in science or philosophy which will be mainly for "in our times" or "for our times." Man cannot risk the loss of his soul by basing his life on scientific findings, which are the results of theories that appear factual but have not been definitely proven.

Much stress is put upon the word "assume" and much error developed, not only by the learned scientist but by others who organize religions and base them on assumed and false connections with John the Baptist, the sages of Tibet, the Pyramids of Egypt, etc. They build up a fake ancestry, inheritance, and an assumed origin, while trying to adulterate or destroy the history of the only original Church and religion, stemming from Christ, Himself.

III

When Christ founded His Church, He conferred upon Peter, the Apostle, the authority to govern His sheep. St. Peter was the first Pope. After him came many others. The supreme authority was always in one head, the Pope. He resides in Rome, although it is not obligatory for him to be always there. He can reside and legislate from any part of the world. When he legislates, speaking ex cathedra, that is from St. Peter's Chair, on any matters or questions of faith or morals, he speaks infallibly, meaning he cannot make a mistake or teach error in those matters. The Pope is recognized, as he has been through the centuries, as the only head of the Catholic Church, but Catholics do not owe him any civil or political allegiance.

Even Martin Luther, the originator of the Protestant Reformation, paid homage to him. When he wrote to Pope Leo X, he said: "I acknowledge your voice as that of Christ, who presides and speaks in you." At another time he reports: "If Christ had not intrusted all power to one man, the Church would not have been perfect because there would have been no order, and each one would have been able to say that he was led by the Holy Spirit."

Christ founded His Church to transmit His teachings to all mankind. Catholics are bound to obey His teachings and not the precepts of Judaism, or the Mosaic law (Acts 15). His Church had been teaching and preaching His instructions before any words of the New Testament were written, and before it was completed, and for centuries before the Bible was formed. Every word of the New Testament was by her children, the Apostles, and not by Christ, who never saw one of the many books that compose it. The Bible is only a child of the Catholic Church and not its mother.

Furthermore, the Bible alone has not been, is not now, and can never be a satisfactory guide as to what to believe. The Church existed four hundred years before its canon was determined; there are many passages difficult to interpret correctly, and St. Peter, St. Paul, and St. Luke warn us about them; also the book does not present fully and clearly all of the truths of our religion. St. Paul emphasizes the importance of our believing not only the written word but also word of mouth: "Therefore, brethren, stand fast, and hold the traditions which you have learned whether by word, or by our epistle" (II Thessalonians 2:15).

To interpret the Bible, the living interpreter must have Divine authority. Just as the Constitution of the United States, or of any of the single states, needs a Supreme Court to interpret it, the Bible needs the Church, which has the authority to do so.

It is well for us to refresh in our minds the truths God has handed down to us through His Son, Jesus Christ. In the strain and turmoil of our daily life, when we become confused and doubtful of things, we should resort to meditation upon the indisputable teachings of faith given to us by God, Christ, and the Church, because they are food for the soul, providing it with renewed energy, determination, and fortitude against the false allures that would blind us and lead us to failure and despair, and ultimately to eternal damnation.

We do not regret our subjection to the Church, because therein one will find that the result of submission is not like having one's freedom cramped or restricted, but the opposite. One will be overwhelmed with the feeling of liberty, the glorious liberty of belonging to God.

In older days, Catholics knew more about their Church and religion, and were staunch, earnest, and true to their God and Church, because they spent more hours attending various services, listening to long sermons, and attending to many different religious activities. They grew up trained to love God and Jesus, and not to fear them. We can take example from them. It does not imply we should have no sense of sin or punishment, but emphasis should be on Love.

In the present era, members of our Church, in spite of the repeated warnings of Christ about false prophets, lend their ears to false teachings and doctrines as prophesied in II Timothy 4:3-4: "For there will come a time when they will not endure the sound doctrine; but having itching ears, will heap up to themselves teachers according to their own lusts, and they will turn away their hearing from the truth and turn aside rather to fables."

This could be a reference to our present-day living and to the spread of Communism, which Catholics have been, in a great sense, responsible for. Like others, they fall for the fables in Communism, the bait for the ignorant, claiming that the State will make living and working easier and more pleasant; a paradise on the earth. But Communism has not done this and cannot do it. Communism cannot exist outside of a slave state. It is an ideology of many erratic concepts, which are carefully hidden from the ignorant, because otherwise they would not fall for it.

Communists infiltrate all activities and all high offices of the community and of labor. Catholics knowingly vote people into important positions, who have openly revealed themselves as in favor of the leftists, or seemed tainted with leftist or so-called liberal sympathies. They have given moral support to the enemies of Christ for their fabled betterment of the earth. They have ignored their religion.

A community has the power of the law to force a man to obey its rules and regulations, because it has the power and is able to take immediate physical action; the Catholic Church has not the power of the law to take physical action against any dissenter or violator of its rules in its ranks. A transgressor can ignore and ridicule the actions of a church against him and fall away from its membership, knowing he cannot be forced or harmed physically. The only resource the Church has is to excommunicate him and leave it to God to do justice in the hereafter. As this is a severe punishment, the Church harbors no love for its execution, hence, she is not hasty in dealing it out to those in contempt of her laws, rules, and regulations. In her suffering, she keeps patient and merciful, ever praying that the sinner may come to reason and change his ways.

IV

Why is a sinful man so contrary to God? Man, being a son of God, owes his allegiance to Him and is bound by His laws. Being one of the family of the Creator's children, he breeds contempt for his Heavenly Father; as the old sayings put it, familiarity breeds contempt; like the hero who is no hero in his own community; like the underdog who hates his master, man had developed within himself a hatred for things of God, because they interfere with his immoral liberty.

Among certain Protestant sects we have people who profess a faith, but who need devotionals mixed with parlor games or beach parties. They have a poor idea of what real religion is. There is something lacking in the faith they profess, or lacking within themselves. God gave us the Commandments; and Christ, His teachings; and they are to be accepted and lived up to with responsibility. Whoever needs a lollypop to be coaxed to work for his soul's salvation is heading for the wrong place. His religion is a sham, and lasts only as long as there is an inducement of some sort or pleasant company remains.

It would be absurd to believe that the churches are responsible for this lack of love of God, and for the coolness toward faith, as well as for delinquency and crime. It is the failure of the sinners to know their religion well and to keep up with it; and to regularly and voluntarily attend their church and services without needing coaxing. The facts support this. Not all people who go to church are honest; some go for show and some to prevent neighborhood gossip. When they leave their native town and move to a distant place, there they conform to their real selves, they rarely show up in a church, and live their lives irreligiously and possibly immorally, because that aura of local shame and decency has been discarded, and because they think their new neighbors do not know them, and that the local habits of the new place are unrestrained. Immorality, crime, antisocial conduct, and other evils are predominant in their offspring.

Some people obey the moral laws of their church as long as the public laws and the local community back them up. When the upholders of decency become lenient in matters contrary to religious tenets or morality, these people thumb their noses at their God, Church, and religion and live according to those lenient public laws, because they make things "legal" for them.

Others live in doubt, because if there is no understanding, there is no sympathy. They may be told not to do this or that, but, unless they have some idea as to why they should not do it, the admonishment becomes merely an irksome restriction which, sooner or later, they break.

Some call an individual who does not drink, smoke, swear, or gamble, and does his religious duties, a good person, but in their minds they harbor a dislike for him. By their moral standards he is doing wrong things; he is doing things they do not do; he is making himself a person apart from their circles; he is committing anti-communal sins. Their egos reveal that religion is not something to their liking. They lack real religion, they lack love of God and neighbor. Many have warped religious concepts which keep them away from church attendance; these attitudes have been mostly developed in their formative years due to lack of positive training, and mostly through parental negligence. It is the parents who are mainly responsible for the nonchalant living of their offspring, who in most cases possibly inherited the evils from them. It is a parental responsibility to bring up and train children right; to teach them mental prayer and make it penetrate. They should not depend wholly upon the church and school, because these are only implements of assistance to them. "A good tree produces good fruit and the assistance of the farmer makes it better."

The first twelve years of a child's life are of potential importance. These are the years the training of the child should be attended to very diligently; it should be done by the parents and not given to the state or other agency—outside of church and its school. During these years the training influence can shape a child's character in the way the parents desire, because this is the time home influence is greatest. The child also has to be taught the meaning of restraint. If he does not learn, he will turn out to be one more egotist, misfit, and coward. During this age, it is most important that the child should be taught so that the teachings and training will sink deep into his mind and take permanent hold there, so that in later life the teachings and training can express themselves.

Every child, until the time arrives when he is considered mature and able to labor and care for himself, should be subject to his parents. When such a time comes, should it be at or before the legal age as set by the country or custom, it would be up to the parents to liberalize or minimize the subjection.

The reactions of grown-up children to an aging parent reflect some of the poor training, or the small amount of good training, absorbed from that given them by their parents in their younger years. Every child is responsible for the keep of his aging parents, if good cause exists, as they were responsible for him in his youth. The more children, the more this responsibility should be divided and shared.

Children are not, in themselves, so much of a problem to our priests, Sisters, teachers, activity supervisors, etc., as their parents are. Parents love to interfere in all kinds of affairs; to make complaints regarding treatment of their child, or look out for favors for their offspring. If something irritates them about the church, school, gymnasium, or social affairs of the child, or the young one comes home with a story made up by his great childish imagination, they should stay home and not be running over for arguments or for meddling. If the child has to fall back upon the parent all the time, he will become a pest, a misfit, or a juvenile delinquent. Stop coddling him! Give him goals to achieve; let him fight his own battles, and make him produce to get compliments. Make him work hard for what he gets, and he will someday be thankful to you! Pampered kids are poison!

V

Man goes to church reverently, because he believes in God and considers it as a home of the Lord. He goes not for the crowd, music, singing, gossip, or other distractions. He believes in God and wants to be with Him closely, in prayer and meditation. He goes in reverence for the mysteries of his faith, though he knows little of them. He goes because the church is a factor for good. He goes, because he can get things there not offered anywhere else, and he can get along better with them than without them.

There is in every church a small percentage of hypocrites who appear at the services and other meetings merely to put on a show for business, politics, or other selfish purposes, but the majority of the faithful attend because they consider themselves as sinners and need the help of their religion for the good of their souls.

In the church we find many varieties of characters, but it is not for us to judge them, if we wish not to be judged. It is not by driving away people from the church, but by cultivating them wisely, that they become valuable to themselves, to the church, and to others.

Some complain that evil people go to church; if so, must we compel them to live right? Coercion in matters of personal thought and behavior are not good. Man gains more by suffering his fellows to live as seems best to themselves, than by compelling each to live as seems good to the objector. There were people in Christ's day who condemned Christ and said He was possessed of the Devil, and would have stoned Him.

If a man does not want to go to church because there are a lot of hypocrites there, let him not forget that the earth has plenty of obnoxious people living on it. He should observe that, and if he does not like it get himself shot off to the moon or some other distant place. In church we have all kinds of people; it was not set up for one variety and it takes care of them all, as in Nature the sun shines and the rain wets and nourishes our growing foods and flowers, as well as the poisonous plants and obnoxious weeds.

We must respect the rights of one another, for the Church is not for one kind, but for all, be they saints or sinners. Saints, in fact, are holy and saved, and do not need a church or salvation, but the sinner does. Christ mainly established His organization to enable the sinners to become saints. The materialist, the atheist, and others, who do not go to a church or have a religion may consider themselves as saints, but they are saints of a different color and heading for the wrong regions.

Men do not know how to live in mutual adjustment with each other. There is a vast reservoir of good will in this world, but man does not resort often enough to its use. He does not respect others and ignores the injunction "Thou shalt love thy neighbor as thyself." Many of his troubles arise because of the differences in his mental and emotional make-up and lack of mental prayer.

Man is changeable in his reasoning; one moment he may be a saint, the next a sinner, or both at the same time. In one breath, he may punish error and admire virtue; by turns, he can be nasty and noble; he can be selfish just when he is unselfish; and he can be straightforward while being a hypocrite. If you complain about someone being bad when he is doing good, you overlook this peculiarity in him, or possibly you consider yourself holier than him, so you condemn him, when in reality, if you were judged at the moment, you might seem more evil than he is. It is not up to us to judge others, but do our moral duty as concerns ourselves.

Moral law demands prompt obedience from everyone; it does not advise what to do, but tells what you are obliged to do. The natural consequences of the disobedience of the law, without fail, is punishment.

Our religion has many practices. To show how good a co-religionist you are, can you answer affirmatively to any or all of these? Do you know the hours the Angelus is rung and do you pray it? When the church bell tolls at a funeral, do you say a prayer for the deceased? Do you make local pilgrimages? Do you go to Mass or other services with a rosary, a missal, or a prayer-book? Do you pay reverence to God and Christ when in church, or do you gape around, daydream, or carry on conversations as if you were in a theater? Do you say your prayers before and after your meals? Do you follow the old custom that the main meal at home has to be a family gathering; that all the members should eat at the one table together with the appropriate prayers? Do you know how to receive a priest at your home on a sick call? Do you begrudge God your donation to the support of His Church? Do you express your cheapness in giving the smallest coin you have? If you have children, do you teach them the importance of helping and supporting their religion, financially and otherwise? Do you know that many of the young people, when they grow up and start to support themselves, lack this training?

These are a few questions a good Catholic should answer easily and affirmatively. If you cannot, your knowledge of your Church and religion is weak and you are a poor Catholic, a fringist.

Though we are all born as introverts and as selfish individuals, we do not need to stay that way. We can make ourselves over if we try. We do not need to spend our lives in complete comfort, because that is bad; it is pernicious to our health; it retards our progress to salvation, as well as our progress for betterment in other ways. Suffering discomfort, we can offer it to God for our own good, in the hereafter, and for the good of the departed; besides, discomfort stimulates us to better things.

There are persons who put themselves into debt up to their

neck, as one would say, so that they can have everything at once, but make no allowances for the support of their church and parish, which was ordered by Christ and is their moral obligation to observe. They put their money into houses, mortgages, cars, travel, and other luxuries, but budget none for the upkeep of their religion. They work extra time, or at extra jobs, which could provide an extra fund for church and charities. They cannot, and do not want to, think of it. Most of the debts they have are not necessary. Why must everything be bought at once? Because they are in debt with a mortgage, they cannot consider it a debt because it really is an investment; a thing that makes you rich! Hence, in getting richer, you are not being excused of your moral obligations; you are not being excused because to gain the world you are losing your soul!

V I

Man is perplexed by mysteries. Christ revealed to us many mysteries which are contained within His Church. There is no need to be perplexed by these mysteries. If we believe in Christ and acknowledge Him as God, we accept the mysteries with full faith, because the mysteries are no concern of ours; they were given to us for our information; they are affairs of God and belong to Him. We are here to accept and acknowledge them, not to question them.

Christ revealed that there is a Trinity; three persons in one God. When at the Last Supper, He spoke to the Apostles: "Dost thou not believe that I am in the Father and the Father in me? The words that I speak to you I speak not on my own authority. But the Father dwelling in me, it is he who does the works. Do you believe that I am in the Father and the Father in me?" (John 14:10). Then again He said: "But when the Advocate has come, whom I will send you from the Father, the Spirit of truth who proceeds from the Father, he will bear witness concerning me" (John 15:26). "When he, the Spirit of truth, has come, he will teach you all the truth. For he will not speak on his own authority, but whatever he will hear he will speak, and the things that are to come he will declare to you. He will glorify me, because he will receive of what is mine and declare it to you. All things that the Father has are mine. That is why I have said that he will receive of what is mine and will declare it to you" (John 16:13-15). "All things that are mine are thine, and thine are mine; and I am glorified in them" (John 17:10). "That they may be one even as we are" (John 17:11). "Even as thou, Father, in me and I in thee" (John 17:21).

God reveals to us who He is but not what He is. He is no subordinate of ours that He should give an account of Himself to us. We are here not to inquire of, or question Him, but to do what He has ordered and to believe in His word.

We have minor trinities that we take cognizance of, although we do or do not understand them, as the trinity of Spirit, composed of God, angels, and man; the family trinity, made up of husband, wife, and child; and the trinity of color—red, blue, and yellow, from which we can produce thousands of tints and shades. As we can have such minor trinities, why cannot there be a Major One, which is God's private affair?

At the Last Supper, Christ instituted the Holy Eucharist, when He "took bread and blessing it, he broke and gave it to them and said, Take, this is my body. And taking a cup and giving thanks, he gave it to them, and they all drank of it; and he said to them, This is my blood of the new covenant, which is being shed for many" (Mark 14:22-24) (Matt. 26:26-28). Also, "And having taken bread, he gave thanks and broke, and gave it to them, saying, This is my body, which is being given to you; do this in remembrance of me. In like manner He took also the cup after the supper, saying, This cup is the new covenant in my blood, which shall be shed for you" (Luke 22:19-20). Here in every crumb of bread and sip of wine Christ was complete.

The Eucharist is bread and wine changed into the body and blood of Christ. We are taking Christ's word for it; we believe in Him and in His word, anything is possible with Him. Why unnerve ourselves about it? He says so, so it must be so! We cannot understand it, but it is not impossible. We change bread and wine into our body and blood, when we eat and digest same.

Steam, rain, snow, and ice, all constitute the same substance, the same elements of water; why cannot Christ be in the Eucharist despite of its appearance of bread and wine? He is a Spirit, He can be everywhere.

As everything, so is bread and wine composed of electrons, protons, and neutrons. In various combinations they produce our elements, and these, in combinations, produce everything in this world; everything in the universe. Why cannot God, our Lord, who created them, have access to the electronic particles and elemental substances, and change their combinations to produce His body and blood combinations? The space about these electronic particles and elemental factors is too small for us to see, but for God it is possible. He can change things there and produce immediate miracles. Because bread and wine do not change their visible forms for us, it does not mean it is necessary, because many elements in their physical or chemical changes maintain a visible form almost alike to each other, and they possess a taste, or no taste, similar to one or another, but mostly by their actions and properties a scientist discerns the difference.

It must not be forgotten that God deals not only in the seen world, but also in the unseen realm. However matter appears to us on this visible earth, it appears different looking at its other aspect. A man's body seems of a mass to us and is visible, but if we eliminated all of the unfilled space in that body and collected all of its electrons, protons, and neutrons into one mass, the man would be reduced to a speck just visible with a magnifying glass.

Anybody differing with Christ on His Holy Eucharist, or other doctrines, is ignoring the importance of Christ as God, an all-powerful God. He is opposing Him as if he were Christ's equal, and Jesus were no more than any other man. This insults the Son of God.

Anyone who does not want to believe and denies the Divinity of Our Lord, or the Holy Trinity, or the Holy Eucharist, even the Primacy of Peter, as well as the existence of Heaven, Hell, and

Purgatory, is making himself liable to perdition. "And shall cast them into the furnace of fire; there shall be weeping and gnashing of teeth" (Matt. 13:47-50).

By his human acts man walks to God; and in these acts he enjoys freedom. His final destiny lies in the proper use of this freedom; he must not abuse it if he wants to come to his ultimate goal, the Vision of God in the timeless world. What the Almighty has revealed it is his duty to accept, if he believes in Him, and question not the wisdom and omnipotence of the Ruler of the Universe.

VII

For over nineteen hundred years the Catholic Church has observed that every now and then a certain human being manifested every sign of being two or more persons in one; two or more characters in one organism; this was called "possession."

Before Christ's time a possessed person was declared to have an unclean spirit besides his own.

The use of forcible and dramatic language, administered by authority, if persevered in long enough, frequently but not infallibly, had the effect of banishing one of these apparent personalities. Prayers and fasting helped also. This was called "exorcism." There was no activity of the Church more mocked than was this.

In the past few decades, it had been discovered that these events did take place and are still taking place in every corner of the world. There is hardly a modern psychologist of repute today who is not familiar with these phenomena, and who does not fully acknowledge the facts. No matter if he calls the first "alternating personalities," and the second "suggestion," at least he acknowledges the fact. This "possession" is a manifestation of the spiritual, as well as an evidence of a spiritual world.

For ages, Christians, pagans, and others believed in angels. The most learned of all religions assumed that there must be something or someone between God and man. Man is a spirit with a body; an angel is a spirit without a body, intermediate between God and man. Who does not believe in spiritual values does not believe in angels; who does believe, believes also in angels.

Angels, being spiritual beings, have intelligence, free will, and power; they were created by God to know, love, and serve Him in Heaven; to be His messengers and to guard men. Their existence is an article of our faith, supported by Holy Scripture and Christian tradition.

Christ mentioned their existence. For one example we can cite Matthew 13:37-42: "He who sows the good seed is the Son of Man. The field is the world; the good seed, the sons of the kingdom; the weeds, the sons of the wicked one; and the enemy who sowed them is the devil. But the harvest is the end of the world, and the reapers are the angels. Therefore, just as the weeds are gathered up and burnt with fire, so will it be at the end of the world. The Son of Man will send forth his angels, and they will gather out of his kingdom all scandals and those who work iniquity, and cast them into the furnace of fire [Hell] where there will be weeping, and the gnashing of teeth."

The Sabbath is the seventh day of the week and the Jewish day of rest. Christian law changed the day to Sunday in honor of Christ's Resurrection. The Ten Commandments state that the Sabbath Day be observed, but does not mention or specify what day. As Christ established the new covenant and His teachings as the basis of our religion, and as we are not subject to the Judaic or Mosaic laws, we select our own dates in honor of our Founder and Redeemer.

A word for marriage. Marriage was originated by God and made a sacrament of the Church by Christ (Eph. 5:21-33) (Matt. 19:6). "For this cause a man shall leave his father and mother, and cleave to his wife; and the two shall become one flesh." This unity means all in one, as God, the Father; Christ, the Son; and the Holy Spirit are united in one God, but separate to each other. Husband and wife are one in unity but separate in body. They unite to produce the trinity known as the "family"—husband, wife, and children.

Marriage is a sacred union between a husband and a wife. In this union the wife is subject to the husband, and the children, when they come, are subject to the parents. The wife is the "soul" of the home, the one who makes a house human and livable for all. She is its interior light and happiness. A selfish and vain woman disrupts a home and is a source of much friction and sorrow. A husband's duty is to maintain, direct, and support a home and a family. A delinquent husband falls very short of his great moral obligations.

A married person does not give divided love to his mate if he also loves his children. A person can love God and country without division. This division exists only in the mentality of the atheist or the enemy of the Church.

Marriage is a lawful state of life. Its primary purpose is the procreation and the bringing up of children; and its secondary purpose is to serve as a sedative to concupiscence; the cultivating of mutual love and mutual happiness. It was instituted for the purpose of propagating the human race and species, and the establishment of a family, whereby the offspring could be brought up with protection and be educated in the proper moral and upright manner until the time when he becomes mature and can maintain himself. Childless couples desirous to have a family can adopt children so as to be up to par.

The taking of anti-fertility pills or compounds to control or prevent birth of offspring is against Nature's law, which demands that marriage's main and primary purpose be the procreation of offspring and the propagation of the species and nothing else.

Marriage is not a gift given to Caesar, it was established by God, and His law takes predominance over the law of the land. The latter can only legislate marriage for those who have no religious bonds; but for others who are members of a church, the law of the land is in duty-bound to uphold God's laws, the sanctity of marriage, and the maintenance of a family. The national law has no right to destroy or impair the unity of wedlock. "What therefore God has joined together, let no man put asunder" (Matt. 19:6). It is the meddling of the lawgivers in sacred affairs that produces licentiousness, adultery, and divorces. Where the law fails in its duty to uphold righteousness, abuse of the moral laws is reckless and abundant.

Uphold what is God's, for those who are of God and members of His Church; punish those who traffic in sin against God's regulations; against the moral law!

The sanctity of the marriage vow, of the home, and of moral living, would not be taken lightly if the national law did its duty to enforce the maintenance of marriage obligations.

VIII

The Catholic Church has come up through the ages, is now, and will be in the future, suffering abuse and attacks on its integrity and existence. Any man who has entrusted the keeping of his immortal soul to his church has the right to defend it with whatever means he possesses. We have been slapped on one cheek and then on the other; after this, it is up to us to do what we can or think is best for our own and our Church's defense.

It is not proper for a Catholic to leave everything upon the shoulders of our priests and religious, to defend the Church and our religion. We must stand up as laymen and not wait on the coercion of a priest, or someone higher up, to do battle with our enemies. Of course, we must use proper judgment in each case.

Lawmakers and others trespass upon the religious domain; upon the rights and liberties of the members of the Church; and expect our priesthood to be silent. Our priests have a right, not only as citizens of the country, but as shepherds of their sheep and custodians of the spiritual welfare of members of their church, to protest and condemn the trespassers and their work, from the pulpit or otherwise.

The government meddles and interferes in many matters which belong to the Church and religion. It is the duty of every community to uphold the laws of God and all moral tenets. They have no right to trespass upon religious liberties. Every Catholic, like his Protestant brother, has rights concerning the welfare of himself, his household, and his children, and the government has no right to ignore them and make rules and regulations only for favored citizens.

Most of our laws are for the good of the general public, not for a particular individual or small complaining group. Why should such minorities have their notions backed up by a court against the general public?

The Reformation was the Protestant Inquisition. The Communistic Inquisition and Persecution is thousands of times worse than the former. In parts of Europe where Protestantism was getting the upper hand, priests and religious were murdered. The outstanding Catholics, as well as those who persisted in their original faith, were slain, their properties seized or burned. The Communists surpass these outrages a million times over. They have killed not only millions of individuals, but have annihilated whole nations. Vast territories have been depopulated and huge slave camps established in the wastes and wilds of Siberia.

During the Reformation in Protestant lands, all Catholics were ordered to attend local churches, manned by Protestant zealots, the majority of whom had not been ordained to their ministry, to listen and be harangued for hours with lies and inflammatory speeches, with the purpose of making them into good Protestants and enemies of the Roman Church; the Communists use the same kind of tactics and call the torture brainwashing.

Protestant historians, to justify Reformation incidents, called them revolts. The Communists justify their actions with the writings of Karl Marx, Lenin, Stalin, and others.

A barbarous or ignorant people (nation) has never produced any books or manuscripts about their history. Catholic countries, not being in such a state, as well as people of other faiths under Communistic domination, have passed down much history and literature, but this is all being destroyed, or adulterated, by the followers of the hammer and sickle.

Throughout the ages, the Church founded by Christ has withstood wave after wave of attack and persecution; it is still here and will continue onward, while the efforts of the persecutors will become dissipated, and will disappear into oblivion. Catholic action and prayer were effectual in the past, and can be in these times.

Prayer is the raising of the mind and heart to God. It may be vocal, mental, physical, or instrumental. It can be in the form of words, singing, labor, charity, or in the form of placing flowers, lights, or candles before any representation of Christ, the Virgin, or Saint, in honor and petition. A representation gives depth to a prayer; it concentrates the mind upon the Mind of the one prayed to.

There are four purposes of prayer. They are adoration, thanksgiving, reparation, and petition. Prayer is as a thought, which, in no matter what language it is expressed, is of the same structure and quality everywhere.

Prayer takes men's minds away from their trials and brings about communion with that which is unseen and abiding. It spiritualizes mankind's sufferings, and places them in a truer perspective. It is an act of trust in the Creator, as well as an act of humility and submission to His Will. It must be sincere. In emergency and peril, it often has added power. A petitionary prayer may not be answered, because you may be asking for a preferred action, or favor, like wishing for rain when someone else does not. You cannot manipulate God through your praying.

When we pray memorized prayers, let the mind be attentive, otherwise the brain will keep bringing them forth, while the mind becomes distracted with other thoughts, making the prayers mechanical and of less value.

Those who pray fervently appear convinced, in most instances, that their petitions are heard and answered, though only infrequently do these answers come in the form of dramatic "supernatural" events. Often, the reply comes in a multitude of ways that cannot be anticipated. In most instances, there is no sudden change, but rather an orderly unfoldment in which things work themselves out. The mechanics of prayer are complex and difficult to understand. There are physical laws which God deems must take their course, but of which, at the time, we are ignorant. We pray and pray, and receive no answer, until some day later we learn of a course of events the laws took and that our prayers were not necessary.

The Holy Church expects us to pray for temporal and spiritual goods and for blessings; that health of body be important to us; that freedom from sorrow, in this world, rightly may be expected; and that happiness would mark us as genuine Christians.

I X

The Bible encourages prayers for the living and for the dead. Moses, by himself, prayed to God and obtained pardon for 600,000 armed men. Angels pray for men; the visions and visits of angels, as described in the Bible, reveal the practice; Jesus spoke about it; and the angelic visits to the three children of Fatima gave evidence that angels are interested in men, help and pray for them.

People, many times, have been uncertain which course of action would best serve a certain "practical" purpose. They have prayed to be enlighted, and were granted the favor.

When you learn to pray, you will find help has been there all the time.

Even atheists pray unconsciously when they are in danger.

People who are allergic to themselves because of self-love should not only pray, but should work and share with others.

Prayer is excellent and indispensable; but prayer—even the highest and holiest kind—is not sufficient, in many cases, if it is not helped with action.

Nobody has ever had to pay for indulgences. Prayer with indulgences is a richer prayer and earns more for oneself, or for those for whom it is offered.

Prayer is like a lamp unto your feet, the light of which dispels the fears and apprehensions of the darkness of doubt, misery, and misfortune, and leads you to the sacred presence of your Redeemer, from whom help and protection shall be given.

Prayer soothes anxiety, helps fight evil, and pleads for Heavenly assistance.

Pray and sing the praises of the Cross, but be not as some Protestants who do the same, but would feel it contemptible to put a Cross upon their church.

Pray the Mass often, weekdays included, and have same offered for yourself, as well as for those dear to you, living or departed. Attend the Mass and do not leave it to the priest to pray it alone for you or your intentions. Bring your friends, too.

The Catholic Church condemns the worship of images as idolatry, but sanctions reverence for the images and holy pictures of Christ, Our Lady, and the Saints. God forbade idolatry, that is, the worshiping of images, but did not forbid the making of them. He forbids the making of them in cases where they are to be adored and worshiped, especially in place of Him and not for His glory. Otherwise, would He go against His own law? Because, in the Commandments He gave in Exodus 15:18-20 we find He ordered the Jews to make images of angels.

A Catholic praying before an image is not praying to the material of which the statue is made; although to an observer it may seem so, because of his ignorance of the situation. You do not pray to or adore your bed and mattress when you kneel before it at night for your retiring prayer, do you? When we speak and pass our thoughts vocally from our minds to that of another person, we do not direct them to the flesh and bones of the person addressed; we speak from our minds to the other's mind, and so it is in prayer.

If statues and holy pictures are immoral in our churches, why are not the statues of kings and heroes; the pictures of our friends and relatives; the Statue of Liberty; the Liberty Bell; the memorial arches and other memorials, immoral and idolatrous? Why not claim the saluting of the flag and military officers as idolatry? When you venerate the photo of your parent and kiss it, are you venerating the piece of paper? Or is it a tribute of love and respect to your parent? When you kiss a Cross, you kiss it not because it is wood or metal, but because it stands for Christ and His sufferings for mankind. If one reverences the pictures of his mother or father, why not revere the representations of Christ, His Mother, and the Saints?

The Catholic's interior mentality may be misjudged by his exterior conduct by those who do not understand. Everything in life that we see is only a picturization of the beings, things, scenes, and actions in our mentality. These picturizations bring to the mind various thoughts, ideas, and knowledge; they influence our emotions. Images, medals, and holy pictures, also sacramentals, bring a picturization of a reverent and emotional content upon the observer's mind, and give effect to his prayers. The presence of the images, medals, holy pictures, etc., during prayer give a kind of value or depth to the petitions, and a kind of fervor or ardent feeling to one's praying. Psychologically, they produce an aspect of close relationship between the petitioner and the petitioned. The prayer has personified qualities and emotional value, and is sanctioned by God. As picturization is in the mind, it is also psychological in fostering concentration of the mind and its thoughts to and upon the Mind of God.

Relics are not ascribed any magical virtue or curative powers; they are, at times, occasions of God's miracles. Reverence for them is not idolatry; it is the same as that of images, etc. Writing in the fourth century, St. Jerome says: "We do not worship, we do not adore, we do not bow down before the creature rather than to the Creator, but we venerate the relics of the martyrs in order the better to adore Him whose martyrs we are."

Every country has relics which it venerates. Every country has its graves of great patriots, its unknown soldiers; it has its relics of crowns, homes, and other precious historical landmarks that belonged to, or were used by, its former great men; and these are all venerated. Is that idolatry?

As veneration of relics and other holy things, for the obtaining of favors and for other purposes, has been a custom since the beginning of the Church, it is not an innovation that criticisms should be made against it. It is stupid for outsiders to ridicule people who understand the motives and reasons for the veneration, because they have lived, witnessed, and experienced the things they believe in. Besides, veneration is not of today; the practice has come down through the ages since the time of Christ. Results from prayer and veneration have been revealed and have

132

occurred, and are still manifesting themselves to the believer, as in the past, and will continue on, benefiting the faithful and the honest seeker of the truth.

Understanding, which is a perfection of man's intellect, but not of itself a moral perfection, helps to clear away the appearances of misinterpretation of others' habits or actions, and brings everything into a better light.

X

God sanctioned holy water throughout the Old Testament. As God does nothing uselessly, in ridiculing the practice of the use of holy water one ridicules God. Water has been ordered for the removal of sins at baptism; for the healing of the sick; for various spiritual blessings; and for many other purposes in the Old and New Testaments. In our times, we can find it producing miracles at Lourdes, France, and at many other religious shrines.

As it is with veneration of the persons which our images, medals, or holy pictures may represent, so it is with all of our sacramentals. There is no idolatry or superstition attached to them. Their efficacy depends principally on the power of the Church, and secondarily on the dispositions of the persons who use them.

Among the Catholics, when the clergy and the religious embrace celibacy or virginity for the Kingdom of Heaven, they are superior to those in the married state. Our Lord and the Apostle Paul revealed this to us, and it was defined as a dogma of Divine faith by the holy Council of Trent. Persons making vows to stay in an unmarried state can more easily and freely serve God and their neighbor; and with more skill lead others to the Kingdom of Heaven.

Martin Luther made his vow of perpetual chastity and obedience to the rules and regulations of his religious order; but he transgressed his vow and carried on clandestine love-making and sexual sinning. He tried to have the Pope release him from his vow, but this was impossible, as it was made to God and not to the Pope. The latter could not release him. Luther confessed his secret sins only to a strange priest or held them back, committing sacrilegious Confessions and Communions. This troubled his mind, so he decided to break away from the Church. He set up grounds for attacks upon his Church and religion, the Pope and the priesthood, culminating his activities in the Reformation movement.

This Reformation made an utter mess and confusion of religion.

How can a pagan mind recognize the true religion in the bedlam of so many sects, numbering into the hundreds, all claiming to speak in the name of Christ? The majority of members of the many Protestant faiths are just nominal members, and they do not practice their religion as they should, because they do not really know their faith and what it stands for. If they did, they would not tolerate freethinkers or all those left-wing ministers manning their pulpits. They would have them preach the Gospels of Christ and not the deceitful philosophies of the Anti-Christ.

Communism is anti-God and antireligion. A minister upholding the tenets of an atheistic body by his actions and living, and preaching coexistence, is taking his flock for a crowd of suckers, who are ignorant of their religious responsibilities. When a flock upholds such a minister, they are what he thinks they are.

Protestantism has drifted away from true Christianity so far that the Protestant outlook is abnormal. Their ridiculing the Sign of the Cross and lack of veneration for that Cross itself is inexcusable. Their upholding of sacred obligations as to life, as against birth control and mercy killing; the maintenance of the family, against easy divorce, adultery, and abortion; their putting up of a solid front against all enemies of religion and decency, and of others, has fallen down miserably. An early Christian would be at home among the practical Catholics, but like a fish out of the water among the practical Protestants.

There are some Catholics who observe the nominal Protestants and pattern their mode of life after them. In some European countries you cannot tell the difference between the two. In the United States the same condition is developing. They have fallen down in the practice of their faith and in the upholding of their religion and their Church. They have become indifferent and materialistic, and their places are cesspools of filth. Others judge us by that behavior, and it is difficult to convince them that it is not Catholicism or religion that have failed, but the man who counts himself as a Catholic, but does not live up to Christ's, and the Church's, teachings.

In some of our churches, listless reverence can be observed at the most holy part of the Mass, at the Elevation. This part of the Mass, for ages past, was held as the most sacred of all. At the sound of the bell, everybody would fall on their knees and bow their heads low with reverence, striking their breasts, saying praises to the Lord: "Blessed be the Most Holy Sacrament, the true Body and Blood of our Lord Jesus Christ, now and always, and forever and ever, Amen." Only a worshiper of the Devil Sect would stand erect in the rear of the church, chewing on his hat or hankie, and blaspheme. Today there is no reverence in some of our churches; people ignore the bells; keep their heads up and look about the church, and talk and laugh. The youngsters observe them and act accordingly.

Mass should be attended to the full; the worshiper should be on time and stay to the end. The practice of cutting Mass habitually, coming in late, and leaving too early, that is, immediately after the Communion, without a valid reason, is sinful. You cannot offer a Mass to God which is second-hand goods and expect a pat on the back from your Lord. He sees you and does not desire you to commit a sin in His name.

When the father of a family works diligently and produces or earns enough or more than he needs, the family prospers and advances; when he has not the means or becomes sluggish or lazy, the family lives in poverty and need. The mother cannot be blamed for the father's doings; she hopes for better times, while she looks after the children and their welfare; she suffers from the father's lack, indolence, or lethargy, possibly more than the children. Progress of mankind can be likened to the father; and religion or the Church, to the mother. Progress of man is due to man himself; religion or the Church, like the mother, can only advise and give moral support. All working together can advance more rapidly and peacefully. The results would be all the better if the mother, the Church, received better and more decent support from her children.

Miracles

I

THERE ARE THINGS that lie beyond the reach of our faculties, such as are called miraculous, and it behooves us not to presume that they are not true or real. There is no predisposition to seek or assume a supernatural explanation of any event which seems out of the ordinary. The situation is usually such that only a supernatural effort can make the change, and it does so inside the natural order of things.

Marvelous events in past history, as well as in the present age, always had corroborating testimony, but, as nothing here is lasting, corroboration and testimony weaken with time, until they finally become only legends. Because they have become as legends does not mean to say they never occurred.

A legend is a story built around some fact or real occurrence that happened in the past. It happened within a certain place or country, and because of the absence of an elaborate chain of news transmission as we have today, other countries may have taken little or no cognizance of it. In later years, it was still regarded as a fact in its native environment but a legend to others.

The Apparitions of Fatima, in Portugal in 1917, were a fact; and the miracle was witnessed by over 70,000 people; but the inimical materialistic world, hostile to religion; and the press, its transmission of news under the control of Communists and their friends at the time, mentioned little or nothing about the occurrences. They hoped to suppress the facts by silence, so that in time everything would be considered a fable.

Miracles are observable events, or effects, in the physical or moral order of things, which cannot be explained by the operation of natural laws, and which therefore must be attributed to the operation of Divine power. Christ and the Apostles performed both physical and moral miracles. Besides Fatima, contemporary evidence of miracles can be found in the records of Lourdes and the other shrines of France, Belgium, Poland, Mexico, and other countries.

Miracles are manifestations of God's power. He is master of the laws of Nature, because He made and controls those laws. He can set aside those laws and produce effects beyond their power of operation, without disturbing the ordinary course of things. If our wills can exercise control over matter, why cannot the will of the Almighty do the same? He created matter, we did not.

Miracles have no natural explanation. Nature cannot produce something from nothing, or give life back to the dead, or cure advanced organic illness in an instant. When these things happen, they are above Nature and indicate a power above it. Miracles do not violate natural laws in the sense of breaking them. A miracle does not suspend a law, but suspends the application of the law. A natural cause can be restrained from producing its usual effect without disturbing the stability of Nature, as a boy throwing a ball into the air against gravity, where he "overrules" or abrogates gravity.

The power of reason alone is sufficient for anyone to know that the cause of miracles is supernatural. No dependence upon faith is necessary.

God cannot do things that are contradictions, such as asking Him who is infinite to create or produce something that is greater than He; but we recognize His intervention in many unusual occurrences. While we do not know all of the forces of Nature, we do know that they have limits; and there are some things which they can never do, as recall dead people to life; cure disease instantaneously by mere touch; mend broken bones immediately by applying water; or cure organic diseases in a moment by bathing in natural water. No matter how far science progresses, it will never explain such miracles without acknowledging Divine intervention.

People have seen and experienced, hundreds of times, the control of bodily actions exercised by some superior power, when mere bodily desires would have dictated otherwise. They have witnessed and wondered why many predisposing causes produced their activities or effects at a coincidental moment.

There are two miracles which everyone accepts, one is the miracle of birth and the other, the miracle of death. Both are universal and eternal. They have never been logically explained. Can you do so?

All scientists know that in their work, when they observe unexplained deviations or phenomena, they are certain that an unknown existing cause produces them. Radium and the planets Neptune and Pluto were found in an effort to explain strange phenomena. So, in many other instances, when phenomena occur, or appear to occur, so as to produce doubt, surprise, astonishment; or to cause awe, wonder, bewilderment, there must be some agency, or agencies, known or unknown, responsible for them.

These conditions do not appear once in a while, but are constantly happening, in countless different ways, in countless different situations, in all natural instances, with or without special Divine intervention. There is no denying these things, so why deny miracles and the work of Someone behind those phenomena, when they are all of the same category?

II

When mysterious things are explained and known, man regards them as common and pays little attention to them. But still, in the course of Nature, these things remain as phenomena, deviations, interruptions, suspensions, changes, happenings, etc. The mirific moment of their occurrence may be instantaneous, or of some duration; constant, gradual, or intermittent. This mirific moment is the instant or moment when the prevailing law or laws of Nature are interposed, overruled, restrained, or abrogated, by a law or laws, either natural or supernatural. It is the instant or moment when phenomenon, deviation, interruption, suspension of application of law, change, or some other event takes place. The events following may be according to the laws of Nature, or the higher laws of God. Yet, the stability of Nature is disturbed very little, or not at all.

As phenomenon, deviation, interruption, etc., and other events or things do occur in Nature, they leave no impossibility for a miracle of God to materialize, because it is of the same comprehensive class, only that Divine Providence specially intervenes in it; because the agency responsible, directly or indirectly, is the Almighty God.

Fire consumes wood and is extinguished with water. Fire consuming wood follows certain laws. Water, on contact with fire and wood at the mirific moment, interrupts or abrogates a course of Nature and changes the situation. The application of heat or some chemical, in the right proportion and at the right time, to a solid, changes it into liquid or gas; and an earthquake or an accident, at the instant of occurrence, can disrupt a course of events and change a course of Nature. You also see your will exercising control over matter, directing it to its own ends; the actions or results surely appearing as contraventions of natural laws. Our actions are not uniform, they are constantly changeable, interrupting and changing the course of Nature intermittently. Every little action affects some law, because there is no absence of law in Nature.

We see manifestations when religious suggestion accomplishes what ordinary suggestion, even under hypnosis, cannot. The miraculous phenomena are noticeable in the processes during metamorphosis—changes in the stages of growth, as of a butterfly. You have it at birth and at death; and in autotomy, the self-mutilation and regeneration in crustaceous insects; in mutation, that is the abrupt departure in the hereditary characters of a species; in the greatest physical actions to the smallest order; and in many other things.

As in natural instances, so in supernatural cases, the miraculous manifestations exist; here they are part of a miracle performed by the Grace of God.

No one can deny the occurrence of miracles, because they are an established fact. They are happening often, not only at shrines all over the earth, but in many other places and in many different ways, only the Zolaized pretend they do not know of them. Anyone who believes that blind chance was instrumental in forming this universe and producing man, or that life came by spontaneous generation; anyone who believes in these discredited theories surely believes in miracles. Because if there were such things as chance or spontaneous generation, they surely were contraventions. As miracles are considered contraventions, so would chance and the other be nothing else but miracles. To believe in them and deny miracles is contrary to wisdom.

Concerning miracles and miraculous phenomena, the word of the Catholic Church is more acceptable than the word of an inexperienced, limited, or mistaken thinker. She has not only enjoyed wider and longer experience, but has actually been more accurate in her observations. She is aware of the failings of human evidence; she never accepts anything without a thorough and convincing investigation. She follows the directions laid down by Pope Benedict XIV, which are sensible and shrewd on these very points.

Man would like to have miracles be simple and understandable to him, but God, the all-wise, knows if He permitted that, the phenomena would become commonplace to man and would not, thereafter, be called wonderful. And man, having his wish, would ignore the Agency behind them, because man is not grateful, but demanding. He would rather remove God than try to recognize, listen, and pay homage to Him.

As the Creator owes nothing to His creatures, He does not have to do what they demand. He will continue to manifest His powers in miracles and unexplained phenomena, so that His eternal Wisdom and Existence will shine forth brilliantly by aweing, bewildering and astonishing man and keeping him mindful of his Master; keeping him mindful that behind all of this wonderment is the Unknown Agency, his God.

Industry and business do things to attract the attention of people to themselves and to their products. God has His own way of attracting those who want to see and want to know about Him and His works. And He does not have to give an account of His doings to anyone. If you are confounded as to how Christ performed miracles by just allowing people to touch His garments, how He persists in doing miracles for those who, in faith, just touch relics, you have little faith in His Almightiness and Wisdom. You pretend you do not see His Omnipotence working in everything with Absolute Independence; from this Absolute Independence, all dependent things had their beginnings.

Fringists

THE ENEMIES OF THE CHURCH and religion would find it hard to turn people away from their faith if it were not for a certain kind of religionist. These are properly called fringists.

If we visualized a revolving ball of fire, we would notice how a shower of sparks coming out from it forms a fiery fringe about the sphere. These sparks, scattering in many directions, we would notice, become acted upon by outside influences and sooner or later grow dark and cold, while sporadic sparks, shooting out of the core, seemingly possess more heat and fire; and wherever they fall, ignite and set up new fires.

This presents to the mind how in religion, as well as in other matters, we have people who resemble these sparks. Some are loosely associated with their church or organization, and have not the fullness and perseverance of the main body. They are the easiest influenced by outside contacts and seldom put up any defense against their enemies, but usually fall easy prey to them. These are the real fringists.

The sporadic sparks shooting out and setting up new fires are the priests, religious, and all the missionaries of God, who go out to the pagan world to build for Christ.

There are at least three kinds of fringists: the liberal, the ambitionist, and the lax coreligionist.

The liberals are not usually close to their church and do not know religion as well as they should, although they think they do. They are the "know-it alls," and are sufficient unto themselves. They like to advise the church or its members about what is right and what is wrong; or they try to explain religious teachings in a way that is erroneous and harmful. They admit a church affiliation, but, like the many intellectuals or sophisticates of our day, they possess the weakness of falling for evil propaganda. The ignorant can be pitied, but these cannot be excused. They need enlightenment as to what is right or wrong and what is God's and what is Caesar's. They need a rekindling of real faith, love, and charity.

The ambitionists, though they are in many respects like the liberals, still differ in that they are two-faced hypocrites. They use religion and the Church as a cloak to cover their sinister plans and actions. They spread the gospel of the Evil One, while pretending to do good. Anything goes for them, as long as it helps them attain their goals. All religions have some of them in their ranks.

The lax coreligionists form a great number of the members of the church. Though they are not like the former two classes of fringists, they are particularly lax in their religious duties. They are absent from services very often. They daydream when the sermon and services are on. They hate to use a prayerbook or rosary. At home, they rarely glance over a religious paper or book. Worldly thoughts dominate their brains and their actions. In church, there is rarely a prayer on their lips. The house of God gets as much reverence as a theater, and much less support morally or financially.

The enemies of the Lord find a fertile field for planting their false ideas among these lax fringists. The nature of these persons is also reflected in their actions at other gatherings, be they social or political. The wrong kind of leaders, be they in politics or labor, owe much of their success to this type of person.

There is another vast group of people who claim membership in the Church, whom we can class as fringists, but not because of any fault of their own. They are the ones who are scattered about the world, in localities where there are no clergy. They need not only clergy, but also, religious workers to serve and teach them, to bring them closer to the core of the Church.

Why do we have so many fringists? Because most of them have had poor training, or have not retained the good training they received and have become rusty in their religious knowledge. When the pulpit tries to reach their ears, they do not hear or do not retain what they hear. In some churches, the sound of the voice does not reach all. Loud-speakers help, but their lack of clarity is a hindrance. When a person hears sound and cannot make out the words, he gets tired of listening and falls asleep, or daydreams. When the voice is heard, there is attention; the person hears, he thinks, and he acts. That must not be forgotten! Hearing brings out devotion and zeal of a higher level, and keeps the members from falling away from the core of their Church and religion.

In spite of the handicap of not hearing well, a little more interest among the members will do their Church and faith more good. The member must not forget that he has some responsibility toward his church and religion, and should not expect everything from the clergy and the religious.

Let us have "One Lord, One Faith and One Baptism. One God and Father of all" (Eph. 4:3-6).

A person who says he believes in God, but does not belong to any Church, does not believe in God entirely, because he does not live according to God's plan and His Commandments. He is a semiagnostic. God's plan demands a man's belief in Christ, in Christ's Church, and in everything that concerns it, as well that he be a church member. A branch not biding in the tree bears no fruit.

If you do not have faith and have not courage to have faith, you do not have what it takes to meet a crisis.

Sin and Sinfulness

I

CHRISTIAN PHILOSOPHY is not grounded in theory, it is based on three ultimate facts, namely: the reality of the law of conscience; the existence of a responsible will as the subject of the law; and the existence of evil—of evil, per se, not by accident of circumstances, not derived from physical consequences, or from any cause out of itself. The first is a fact of consciousness; the second, a fact of reason necessarily concluded from the first; and the third, a fact of history interpreted by both.

The existence of evil, or sin, is thus a fact of consciousness, a fact of reason, and a fact of history, interpreted by both consciousness and reason.

God did not originate sin; it was originated by man; and the evil influences of this sin permeate the human world. When man committed this Original Sin, he was forced out of Paradise, to labor and sweat out his existence, and was deprived of much of his endowed knowledge. To replace this, he is forced to study and learn, and to take persistent instructions, otherwise he would not be doing very well. He is also incessantly working and striving without end; farming, manufacturing, building, doing research, etc., for the wrath of the Deity has to be appeased.

We do not cringe or grovel because we "fear the Lord" because of our trespasses; our fear and sorrow are no more than that which is the outcome of our trespassing of any civil law of the land, and the reckoning of the consequences. No one lives in a constant certain emotion; neither does God. If He becomes angry, it is a justified anger. There is sin in this world, and there must be justice. He is not going to put a wreath upon the head of a murderer and treat him as the equal of a person who lives a good and sinless life. He must have, therefore, appropriate places of disposal for both kinds.

Concupiscence is inborn in the body and soul of man; in the body, it seeks expression regardless of the intellect and of reason; in the soul, it is the unreasoning and unreasonable self-favoring, without regard to what is right or true.

The history of man proves religion does not pervert a man's mind; it is the evil in the person which conflicts with righteousness that makes itself evident in the man's living and deeds. When his evils predominate in masked forms and find companionship in others, especially in those of his category, these evils become worse.

Our acts are either positive or negative, either for a good or for a bad end. An intention must precede each, and each intention must have a motive. The strength of a temptation for evil equals the sum of the impelling motives minus the sum of the restraining motives. The more susceptible a man is to the restraining motives, the less likely is he to yield to evil and temptation; in other words, the less depraved is his disposition.

The whole course of Nature shows God's power over us, in many instances which imply reward or punishment; men bring misery upon themselves by their behavior; sickness or death, oftentimes, is due to intemperance; habits acquired in youth are often the cause of ruin in later life. These things are not accidental, but proceed from the very general laws by which God governs the world.

If we do good, satisfaction and delight are our reward; if we do wrong, pain, disease, or uneasiness are the consequence. God is our Master, our Ruler! He rewards or punishes us for our actions, in as strict a sense as subjects are rewarded or punished by those who govern them.

The whole analogy of Nature, the whole present course of things, most fully shows that our Almighty Father will reward and punish in the hereafter, as it reveals Him doing so at the present time. These things are not accidental. The law of compensation, with which we are all well familiar, is not accidental either. All proceeds from the very general laws by which God governs the universe in the natural course of His Providence. These things are so analogous to what religion teaches about future reward and punishment that there should be no doubt about them.

Moral government does not merely reward and punish men for their actions, but also does it in an exact proportion to their merits and demerits. God, the Moral Governor of the universe, who established moral law and order, will certainly do the same. His distributive justice will be the completion of moral government, the principles and beginnings of which are noticeable in the existing course of Nature.

Everybody who cares sees God revealed in all creation. Everyone who desires sees His power, bounty, charity, justice, mercy, and will revealed. Why should we have justice and mercy? As everything has its opposite, so these must show that evil and punishment exist.

If a man traveled through either pleasure or pain, he would be traveling through an extremity, and would know only one of the two. But, as we know his path is intermixed with both, it shows he travels up a middle road where he is in touch with each one of them. The greater his swerve to any side, the greater the effect of that side upon him. Our conscience gives an inkling of what to expect in another world, where there are pleasure and beauty, as well as sorrow and pain. Thus are Heaven and Hell indicated in our many discoveries.

Our problem in sinning is one of attitude. We run away too much from responsibilities. We shirk them, although in the end we will have to account for them. Our personality becomes the end product of all the experiences of our life; be they good or evil, each will leave its mark on us and our attitude to some degree.

God speaks to us often in many different ways. "Thou shalt not eat of the tree," but man disregards the command and reaps punishment for his disobedience. Everything taken from Nature, he claims, is good. It is not so! There are things which cause much distress, sickness, and other troubles. There are poisons that kill even if taken in the minutest amounts. So not everything is good in Nature, but also it is not evil, only harmful. There is only evil in man, but harm in Nature. Our sins must be looked upon from their evil side and not from the pleasurable side. If man possesses sufficient power of resistance to the seductions of the Devil, he may be easily led by the Hand of God to gain true happiness.

It is not the motion in the machinery that destroys it, but the friction; and it is not your activities that damn you, but the sin in them. All of the ills that flesh is heir to man brings upon himself by his erroneous or sinful living.

A selfish, indifferent life is like that of one who lives in the brightness of the day and sees nothing beyond; but should he arise and go high above his day, out into the outer layers of space, above the earth, there he would see the stars and the heavens before him. Why wait till it is the Night of Life to see the Beyond?

II

The soul does not obtain its knowledge of goodness, temperance, and justice from experience; it perceives and manifests these Divine virtues within itself, and by itself. It grasps what our senses cannot, and knows the difference between good and evil. It knows that what you sow you will reap, depending on the mercy of God. It understands that in the moral law there is justice, and that justice is of two kinds, rewarding and corrective. Her knowledge is supported by Holy Scripture, which tells that God will render to every man according to his works; if he is in Grace, he receives happiness in Heaven; if he is in mortal sin, he earns damnation in Hell; and if he is in venial sin, not good enough for Heaven or Hell, he must expurgate that sin in Purgatory; for he is not welcome anywhere without the proper justice being done.

God who gave laws to the world of matter is also the Legislator of the world of spirits; and the Author of all moral law. He governs for a purpose. There would be no moral order if this world were not governed for a good purpose. Hitler, Mussolini, Stalin, and their henchmen denied that there was any foundation to morality. Communists and their sympathizers propagate this negative doctrine, causing moral chaos in the world today.

An individual's moral sense can make certain acts repugnant to him. The content of the acts may not be such as to cause others to have the same repugnance, because the acts are rationalized.

The Heavenly Father does not violate our freedom, even when we insult Him. He gave man free will to win Heaven or choose Hell. In our sinning we need no help, because we are quite sufficient unto ourselves. No one is in Hell who had not a chance of earning Heaven.

In sin is guilt and punishment. The removal of one does not necessarily imply the removal of the other. Adam was pardoned his disobedience, yet, in penance and punishment, he had to earn his bread by the sweat of his brow, and finally undergo death. Besides the forgiveness of guilt and the eternal punishment due to sin, there remains some temporal punishment left. Expiation of this occurs in Purgatory.

The Bible encourages prayers for both, the living and the dead. If there is no Purgatory, then why should one pray for the dead? The word Purgatory does not occur in the Bible, but the reality it symbolizes is referred to in both the Old and New Testaments; and in the writings of the early Fathers of the Church, the idea embodied in that word is set forth many times.

Our Lord speaks of the forgiveness or sin in the next world. If the good should go straight to Heaven, and the bad to Hell, why should there be a question of forgiveness of sin in the world to come, if there were no Purgatory?

Besides evidence offered by the Bible and tradition, reason alone suggests and demands that there exist a state midway between Heaven and Hell. A soul burdened with the slightest venial sin must have a place to cleanse itself, because nothing even slightly defiled can enter the heavenly Paradise.

Only the wilfully wicked go to Hell; the perfectly perfect go to Heaven; and those who are neither altogether good nor altogether bad, who leave this world with slight sin, go to Purgatory, because without such a place of purgation they could not be saved.

Man's body depends on food to live and enjoy life and health; without food it would starve and die; the soul does not need food, it lives on good and evil; living on good, it attains to the highest good or God; living on evil, it attains the final evil, Hell and the Devil. Following a middle course, with more good to its benefit, it may get to Purgatory.

As we are told there will be a Last Judgment Day, when everybody must appear, so, then, the souls of the departed, in the meantime, must reside somewhere, either in Heaven, Hell, or Purgatory. And these places must be taken care of by the appropriate angels. Naturally, God would not burden His good angels with looking after Hell, and carrying out the punishments there. So it stands to reason that the fallen angels of Lucifer must manage the places of torment, and the Devil must dominate those regions.

Of Hell we find God spoke ninety times in the Old Testament, and it is mentioned at least fourteen times in the New Testament. It was also revealed at Fatima during the Apparitions.

As we spend much of our lives in avoiding decisions, especially the hard ones, this is just the way we go to damnation, by letting an immediate advantage outweigh our ultimate good. And wrong standards of living that contradict natural law are not standards at all. To adopt standards of life of a materialistic and immoral world is transgressing the natural and moral laws.

It is not our bodies, but our souls, which are capable of receiving either the gift of Grace, or the stain of sin. God gives us Grace to act in conformity with our nature. We remain free to accept or to reject it. If we reject Grace, we will soon find ourselves living in sin and become slaves to our passions. And our pleasures will weaken us and leave us dissipated, dissatisfied, disgusted, disillusioned, and discontented. We should strive for Grace; we should live a good and exemplary life, devoted to the essentials of moral living and the making of a happy environment.

III

In the early biblical days sin was punished by death. Death of the body and not of the soul. At the Last Judgment everybody must appear. If the sinful souls were punished by death, that means by total destruction, as some of our dissenters claim, they could not be present at the Last Tribunal. God would have to re-create them. But why should He re-create new souls to suffer for the souls which have been destroyed and do not exist at that particular time? As the Almighty Father does not annihilate the souls of His children, they will appear. As they will appear, where are they kept in the meantime? Surely, throughout these ages, while waiting, the bad souls were not kept with the good ones? Nor the intermediates mixed with any of either? So there must be a Heaven for the good; a Hell for the damned; and a Purgatory for the intermediates. If God destroyed the sinful souls, then there would be no bad souls to appear on Judgment Day. Only the good and some intermediates would be called. As all "saved" souls would be present, there would be no necessity for a judgment session. We believe there will be a final Day of Judgment, which indicates the damned will be there also.

To the contenders that people are predestined for a Heaven or Hell, meaning some are selected for salvation, while others are marked for damnation, the promise of the Judgment Day is a refutation. If all was predestined, there would be no necessity for a final tribunal. Neither any need for the Commandments, the moral laws, or of the Passion and Death of Jesus Christ. You cannot accuse God of producing hoaxes! Those are all erratic ideas! Beware! He reads your small, cramped, materialistic thoughts in His persevering patience and bides His moment, though, from time to time He sends occasional urges or threats to awaken you out of your lethargy and wanderings, but possibly you do not take notice. You have, as well as everybody else, some good in yourself somewhere, why not bring it out and make it the heart of your endeavor to be better and to understand God and His works better?

Man's purpose on this earth is not pleasure. If we were not to suffer, God would not have endowed us with nerves and faculties to experience pain and misery. And we must not forget that all of that feeling is in the soul, meaning it will be carried over to the next world.

In this existence, we are born possessing vitality and energy. Our bodies at birth are endowed with both to a certain extent. As we go through life, we make demands upon them very often during the day, and every day. Whatever amounts of energy we consume, by food, rest, or sleep losses can be replenished; but what amounts of vitality we use up cannot be replaced. If we live a good and moral life, and avoid all sin and occasion to sin, we can save our vitality and extend the years of our health and abode upon this globe. If we dissipate it away by mistaken or sinful living, we will age sooner and die before our time. Conserve your vitality!

A person may inherit an evil disposition, but in most instances it is an acquired trait. Somewhere in his life such a man decided to act in a wrong way, because it gave him pleasure or satisfaction; and, when finding the proper environment and friends most inclined to sympathize and act in cohort with him, he becomes a problem; and it takes much effort to break his sinful ways. If there is belief in God, intense religious brainwashing; possible solitary confinement; a change of friends and environment, used as means together, may restore him to goodness; but, if he is atheistic in mind and resists, very little can be done for him. If his acts are criminal, incarceration should not be denied him. Such a sinner "lives" in his body, allows his glands and organs to control him; his mind is set for damnation; his will power is settled to act just as he plans and pleases; and his conscience abhors being bothered by God or morality.

The more we impress thoughts or ideas upon our minds, the more they become set there, and the more they influence our behavior or thinking. The more thoughts or ideas we can introduce to counteract other thoughts or ideas, the more power we build up to eradicate them. The more impressions of good, the greater the influence is for the good. A greater success can be obtained if the subject is co-operative.

Children and young people resort to much impressionistic thinking; it is the youth which must be watched carefully in this respect. Parents try to meet life in all details and look to the future, but when their youngster shows a demanding attitude, appropriate action must be taken at once, to enlighten the child as to its errors. They must be told why curtailments and restrictions must be put on wrong behavior. A demanding mentality can develop into a sinful one. Going through life, parents should remember that "it is better that thy children should ask of thee, than that thou look toward the hands of thy children" (Eccles. 33:22).

If to admonishment, a youngster retorts, "What can we do, where can we go?" it should be suggested that he stay home and find something to do there; to help in and around the home; to do some painting, on or in the house or of some of the furniture which needs a touch-up; to mow the lawn or cut the hedges; to weed the garden; to clean the yard, cellar, or attic; to fix the fences or other things needing mending; to wash or clean the car; scrub or wax the floors; or learn to cook. Be the child male or female, it will help in having this knowledge to meet life's problems in the future. Some can get themselves part-time work; develop a hobby, or go fishing. Visiting relatives should be encouraged. This is greatly missed by youngsters; they grow up not knowing who their relatives are, or approach them as if they were strangers. They should be told that their parents owe them no entertainment, neither does their community. Also, that the world does not owe them or anyone a living, but that it must be earned. They should be told that they owe the world their energy, time, and talents. They can help in their own parish affairs, as well as help out as volunteers in their local hospital, or in community doings. They can help the neighboring poor and needy. After all, they can take a walk or do some reading. There is always something idle hands can find to be busy with for their own good.

In this world we have much poverty, which in many homes can be reduced by their own efforts. But if there is sinful behavior by one or both parents, no efforts are made. Where one good parent suffers from the evils of the other, the law does not help to curtail the evil doings of the malfeasant and force him to better his home conditions. These people, as well as others, do not live within their means, be it a time of prosperity or depression; in each, they spend or dissipate their earnings for wasteful or wrong needs. During prosperity they take on more debts, allowing no safety margin for savings, emergencies, obligations, and other eventualities.

IV

There cannot be any light without darkness. The contraries of pleasure and joy are pain and sorrow. We cannot have pleasure and joy without pain and misery existing. Happiness is related to good, while suffering is related to evil. As there are extremes to things about us, the extreme of good is God and Heaven; while the extreme of evil is the Devil and Hell. Logic, the science of correct reasoning, proves the existence of all.

It is well our lives here are short, because of inaccurate diet, evil habits and behavior, and of sinful endeavors, most of them become miserable. If you want to die well, then look forward toward your end; store up enough good provisions for that great day, so that your meeting with the Lord will be joyful not sorrowful. If you want to die happily, love misery on earth. If religion seems a burden, bear it for Christ's sake, because He carried a burden for you. Why wait till sickness or old age overtake you to exercise the virtues, when you can perform good acts while still young and healthy?

As you grow older, your character tends to intensify the personality of your youth. If you were generous, you may become an overly generous older person; if you were stingy, you may turn into a miser, a penny-pincher, and one who grudgingly puts the smallest coin into the collection basket. If in your youth you had evil tendencies, you may develop into a criminal, etc.; and so on, your older days may disclose what kind of a young person you were.

In his daily pleasant existence, man feels and thinks, in his actions and by his environment, that there will be no change in things as they are at the moment; that everything is going to last forever. That feeling he has in his soul, because it, per se, feels eternity, and it fools the body, because there is no thought of things ahead and no preparedness for any future calamities or demands. This same complaisance is usually present in a sinful life. The sinner does not think of, or puts off, repentance to a future date.

The Devil tempts not only unbelievers and sinners, whom he already possesses, but the faithful and devout he tempts and molests more and in many ways. The holier the day is for the person, the greater is the Devil's effort. For weeks, a person goes on living, resisting sin and temptation without great strain, until he comes to the day he makes a Confession and receives Holy Communion. That day he resolves to keep extra holy and sinless; but that very day his efforts have to be doubled, as it seems something works extra hard to tempt him and bring him into mortal sin. The Devil is wrathful that day because he has lost a soul, and is determined to regain it by just one big sin, so then he can relax until the next Confession and Communion.

Of all sin, the sexual sins are the most prevalent. Sexual relations outside of marriage are against the laws of God and Nature. The primary reason for sex is to propagate the species; and it is the duty of married couples to bring forth offspring. When they bring forth children, they do the duty that marriage imposes upon them. Children have no right to resentment against their parents because they came into the world. It was God's wish they were born, and not the fault of the parents.

Illicit love, petting, and debauchery are sinful and harmful, not only to the soul, but to the body also; the sinner will sooner or later pay for his perversion. The law of compensation exists, and it will reckon with each one in this life. Wherever contraceptives are used, the final result may be that both will end up sterile or impotent; the female usually develops various kinds of internal diseases, among which may be tumors or cancers, because these occur mostly from false sex relations.

Where a wife gives birth to a child produced by artificial insemination, from a seed other than that of her husband, the husband has no obligation toward that child, because it is not his body and blood; he is not bound to accept or support it. The child belongs to him from whose seed he was born. This kind of an affair is a case of adultery on the part of the wife, and it is sinful in its scope.

Your sins will find you out is an old saying; if we look about us, we will find much truth in it. The ravages of sin leave their marks on many transgressors. A person who has spent some time in sexual perversion may be marked immediately with characteristic discolored puffs under the eyes and with listlessness; a woman dissipating may reflect characteristic developments of her face, eyes, and body (Eccles. 26:12); if she has borne children, her throat may have a characteristic puffiness about the front of her neck; and if she has desires or tendencies toward immoral sexual thoughts or practices, she reveals them in the style of clothes she wears and in her behavior. Tight skirts and the wearing of slacks, outside of home or work, unless they are indispensable to the occasion, indicate an immoral urge on the part of the teen-ager or grownup.

A man who gets a kick out of the companionship of a woman who loves to dress up in slacks is unconsciously making of himself a homosexual. It seems to satisfy his ego that he is courting and romancing with a man, but is saving face for himself by using a woman as a substitute.

Another incentive to sin, especially fostered by parents in their children, is giving them allowances and not demanding an accounting of their spending. With this money teen-agers romance with the opposite sex and, sooner or later, indulge in sex perversion.

To those under seventeen years of age, "going steady" should not be allowed. "Going steady" is for older couples whose intention is to marry. "Going steady" is responsible for most of the illegitimate children being born. Parents shirking care in this duty will be answerable to God.

Where there are habitual sins of a certain nature, they are results of difficulties with family or friends, inner personality conflicts, or some other fundamental trouble. When these are corrected, the sinners find it easy to discontinue their sinful activities.

V

Birth control by means of contraceptives is a menace to the health of women; it is a hideous peril to future mothers. Contraceptives cause inflammatory conditions, infections, and internal growths. They cause many other female ailments as well as sterility. Men using them also go sterile, or lose their vigor. They detract from the full physiological value of sexual union, producing future harm to the general health, the sex organs, and the nervous system. They are responsible for the high rate of uterine tumors and cancers.

Newly married couples resort to artificial birth control methods, in many instances, because they want to continue working and feel children would be in their way. When the time comes to have children, they find it is too late, that they cannot have any because of their sinful living. You cannot tamper with Nature and not get hurt!

Medical science is intended by God to give us the use of natural means for the prevention and checking of disease, which is not of God's creation but the result of sin in the human race. The Fifth Commandment requires us to preserve and prolong our lives and those of others.

When a child has been conceived within a womb, it is willful murder to produce an abortion to rid oneself of it. It is a mortal sin against the Fifth Commandment. Such birth control is dangerous, producing possible peritonitis and death to the sinner.

In trying to avoid sexual abuses, we must live and think cleanly. When a person indulges in sex abuse, the urge is for more; and the more it is satisfied, the greater becomes the desire, until it is difficult to break away. The less one indulges, the greater becomes his resistance; until the time comes when he will be able to control himself and his passion. To help himself avoid temptation, he must shun all occasion to sin, as in persons, books, places, things, and food, which may tend to stimulate or provoke a transgression. He should avoid all alcoholic beverages, hot spices, cocoa drinks, and other articles of food which may affect the sexual glands. On cloudy days when there is a something in the air that causes the expansion of glands and irritates them, as a change of weather affects a corn on a toe, to prevent temptation, one should be active and keep away from solitude.

Everyone should remember that sex was not given to man for illicit pleasure, to be abused and misused. Chastity and avoidance of evil will benefit the body and soul, and increase your vitality. As body organs are modified by use or misuse, avoidance will strengthen them, while abuse will weaken them.

Disease is a natural consequence of life, but man would not be prone to it if he had not transgressed against the laws of God and Nature, lowered his bodily resistance, and made himself open to its attacks.

The Catholic Church resorts to prayer and sets up hospitals, with religious orders to staff them, to help fight disease. It has also advocated and endorsed reliable means for that battle. The Church has always propounded the teachings of Christ regarding the proverbial Samaritan, and has taught that God helps those who pray and help themselves. It is the religions which profess that prayer alone without help will cure and heal that are responsible to a great degree for epidemics, unnecessary suffering, and unwarranted deaths.

Confession of sin and doing penance for same is God's own will and wish. Man may not dictate to God in this matter or any other. God's way is the right way, whether it agrees with our wishes or not.

Christ gave the Apostles the power to forgive sins, but, as He said they could forgive or retain them, they had to know what the sins were. Hence, they were given judicial power to know specifically what the transgression was. And to know what the sins were they had to be told, hence we have Confession, because "As the Father hath sent me, I also send you. When he said this he breathed on them; and he said to them, Receive ye the Holy Ghost. Whose sins you shall forgive, they are forgiven them; and whose sins you shall retain, they are retained" (John 20:21-23).

The Apostle Matthew writes about Christ's promise to Peter and the Apostles: "Amen I say to you, whatsoever you shall bind on earth, shall be bound also in heaven, and whatsoever you shall loose on earth, shall be loosed also in heaven" (Matt. 18:18). "And I will give thee the keys of the kingdom of heaven; and whatever thou shalt bind on earth shall be bound in heaven, and whatever thou shalt loose on earth shall be loosed in heaven" (Matt. 16:19).

These were the powers given to the Apostles to be passed down through the ages so "that repentance and remission of sins be preached in his name to all the nations, beginning from Jerusalem" (Luke 24:47).

Our Lady of Fatima complained that people do not pray enough. It is true! It can be seen on Sundays at services in the churches; the places may be full of people, but few of them have prayerbooks or rosaries; the large number came merely to be present and spend the time in gaping and daydreaming.

Others stay home and desecrate the holy day by breaking the Third Commandment, ignoring the warning Our Lord gave that such a soul shall perish out of the midst of one's people, meaning will be condemned to Hell. Too frequently on Sundays you will find people sawing wood, hanging out the wash, and carpentering about the home, building or repairing something; and the material and tools used, in many instances, have been stolen from their places of employment. Are these people so short-minded that God will not demand restitution from them for their deeds?

And others forget that the day is a holy day, that it should be kept sacred; and we should wear our finest in honor of Our

Lord, when we travel about our communities, and do not go
about in dirty dungarees.

"The Sabbath was made for man and not man for the
Sabbath" (Mark 2:27).

Death

I

A YOUNG GIRL about fourteen years of age was weeding in her
mother's garden. She happened to look up from her task and
beheld a strange woman hurrying across the field and across the
garden to get to the street. The stranger carried a small vial of
pills in her hands. The girl, surprised, tried to stop the trespasser.
"What is your hurry and where are you going?" she asked. The
woman slackened her pace and answered, "I cannot tarry, my
master's orders must be fulfilled, and I have many of them."
"What do you mean, and what are those pills for?" inquired the
maiden. "Wherever I go, I give one to the person I visit. If he
is weak, he dies; if he is strong, he may live," answered the
woman. Astonished, the young girl demanded, "Who are you,
lady?" "Oh, I have no time to talk, I must be going to that
house," she replied, pointing to a home a little up the road. "I
have to visit the son of those people and then be going to many
other places." And she went off.

The girl gave a glance after her and then ran into the house
to her father. She told him about the occurrence and conversa-
tion. "That must have been an angel of death," he said. "She
must have been of the other world," added the daughter, "because
the grass and weeds did not bend under her feet as she passed
over them." And no sooner had she finished speaking when the
air outside was rent with cries and lamentations. "Help! Help!
My son is dying, help!" The cry came from up the street. The
father and daughter hastened to the stricken home, and found

there was nothing they could do to help save the boy. A priest was called, and he administered the last rites.

This was a true occurrence. Possibly it was an angel of death. The Bible made mention of them.

There are many other ways people picture death. Some draw a skeleton covered with a white sheet; others see it as the moment when the soul leaves and is borne away by either good or bad spirits; and others consider it as the moment when a person, on his deathbed, his life ebbing away, is awaiting the end. There are also other illustrations of the passing moment, but all are of the same category—all are indicative of the separation of the body and soul.

I have witnessed hundreds of persons in the act of dying; not everyone seemed to cease his breathing in the same manner. People die in various ways. In almost all cases that are not too sudden, unconsciousness overcomes the mental faculties. The person does not know if he is suffering, if he actually is; only when moments of consciousness appear, he recognizes pain and discomfort, but that is just for the moment, because he relapses into a coma again, weakening every instant until his last gasp.

No one can explain this miracle of death. No one can do anything to stop it. This transitional period of life on earth to the life beyond has been implanted by God, from the time of Adam and Eve's banishment from Eden.

Death is only a physical phenomenon; our life an inextinguishable process; and our span of existence on earth an anatomical interlude in eternity. From youth to old age, it hovers about. In joy or sorrow it may appear. When skies are dark and tempests scowl, it rides the waves, ready to strike.

Death is just another law of Nature, where we lose our bodies but not our living being. The destruction or amputation of some of our organs or limbs does not destroy our living agent; and so we have reason to believe that we shall not be destroyed by death. Sleep suspends our living powers but does not destroy them. Mortal diseases do not destroy or affect our intellectual powers.

By natural law man enjoys the use of life, but does not have ownership of it. The Almighty Creator gave man life and He remains its owner. He gives to each the use of it, and He will take it back when He is ready. Under certain circumstances God gives to men, and to the state, His permission to take human life. He allows the killing of an unjust aggressor, either in crime or war, but never gives anyone, individual or state, the right to kill an innocent person, be he sick or well.

According to the laws of Nature, nothing is lost. Your spirit will not perish at death; and every atom of your material body will continue to exist until disposed of by God. The survival of the soul is reasonably proven from the spirituality of the soul, and of man's desire for perfect happiness. You cannot have desire for anything if it does not exist. The breaking up of the body cannot end that which was encased within it. The spirit lives on to fulfill its mission. The soul is here to tarry, but not to abide.

Death is the harbor where everyone finds an end to his troubles in this world. It is a landing into eternal happiness or eternal misery. No one knows the hour or the day when he will be called. You cannot live hoping God will give you the opportunity of final repentance, in spite of a life of sin. That would be a sin of presumption against the virtue of hope.

Death is the tragic thing which is only an attribute of living matter, as of bodies, but not of spirit. When it seems far away, men seldom fear it; but when the danger of it is near, then fear and moral desperation arise and hold sway. Man's wisdom, if it does not come about till he is near the verge of dying, sometimes comes too late; because death is certain, always ready, never far off. If the person is sick for some time, he is lucky, because sickness gives him an opportunity to exercise virtues and make amends to his Supreme Master. Why wait? Why not resolve now to better yourself, before your body is stretched in its last-found home, knowing the old no more?

Death is not an affliction, but a punishment for sin upon man. God did not make death. St. Paul says: "By one man sin entered into the world, and by sin death; and so death passed upon all men, in whom all have sinned."

In Ecclesiasticus 39:35 we read: "Fire, hail, famine, and death, all these were created for vengeance." These were created as punishment for sin. Because of Original Sin, everyone, good or bad, is subject to this transitional phenomenon.

I I

Among the mysteries of death, consider the happenings during metamorphosis—body-building changes in the stages of growth, as of a butterfly—where the "field of organization," which during the stage of a larva determines the structure of its body, and the functions of its organs, contracts during the pupa stage and disappears, leaving behind a disorganized mass of living cells in a state of death. Then a miracle happens. A "field of organization" of a new type expands from a particular point in the mass of cells, and reorganizes the cell material, grows a new nervous system, and produces a butterfly. These "organizing" living fields seem to emerge from "another world" into the physical world. In the laboratory studies of these "fields," one observes that at death they disappear into the world from which they came.

All living organisms have been found to be imbedded in complex electrical fields, and these disappear at death. It is hard to escape the conclusion that these fields are independent of the matter involved, and by their innate properties determine the structure and functions of the living organisms.

Our nerve cells are links which connect our physical brain with the world in which our consciousness is rooted. At death, our "brain field" is not destroyed. It contracts and disappears, apparently falling back to the level of its origin. All of our memories are indelibly "engraved" in this field; and after death, when our mind is no longer blocked by inert matter, we can probably recall them all, even those of which we were never consciously aware of during our lives.

In your dreams you see, hear, and speak, but not with your eyes, ears, or vocal cords. The action of your senses is relaxed and suspended, yet you see, hear, and speak. A time will come when your senses will be permanently useless, yet you will be seeing, hearing, and speaking, as easily as you did in your dreams during life.

We know that nothing in this world is destroyed; if it appears to be destroyed, it has only disappeared into the "other world." If anyone claims the soul is destroyed at death, then into what does it perish? Where does the magnetism go when the magnet is demagnetized? Of course, it returns to its magnetic field; as nothing comes from nothing, everything comes from some source and returns to its element. When the soul ceases to animate the body, it returns to its source, God, its Creator, for its disposition. Death takes place only when the soul is separated from the body. The latter, which is nothing more than earthly substance, immediately begins to disintegrate.

Dissenters claim that when God sends death upon anyone, He destroys him completely; can they prove how God will bring the dead back to life if their souls are destroyed, especially when everyone must appear at the Last Judgment?

When a person is lying close to death, in the anxiety of surmising what may be ahead, some truths come to him with an overwhelming force. A ray of reason penetrates his mind. He begins to think of events and attitudes in his life that seemed important to him. He sees more of the things that once he scorned or passed up as of little importance. They appear more in detail than the things he considered more valuable in his daily routine. He desires to repent and save himself. Though he does, this would not lead him straight to Heaven, because there is his penance to atone. He must, nevertheless, expiate his sins after death, possibly in Purgatory, the stopping place on the way to Heaven.

We do not know what sort of punishment is dealt out in the state of Purgatory. It may be varied, but we know that no one returns from Heaven or Hell. But from Purgatory, there may be allowances to souls to communicate, in some manner or form, for help from their relatives or friends. The departed souls do not lose their ability to exert power to get in touch or communicate with living beings here on earth.

When a person dies, our thoughts do not follow the soul, nor do we evaluate the tolling of the bell and the ceremonies. Our impulse is to cling to the corpse, to honor it by solemn burial, costly coffin, and a monument; but very little do we strive to shower the soul with prayers, mortifications, and penances. When one we love dies, our love must be directed toward the soul of the deceased. Not that we should ask God to return the soul to the earth, but we should sincerely pray for its acceptance into His Grace and forgiveness; and that when our time comes we may be reunited with the departed in the arms of the Lord.

Among all the good we could do for the deceased, we must not forget to pray and pray. Prayer for the departed is not an innovation, because prayer for the dead was solicited by the first Christians of the first century; the inscriptions on their tombs disclose the practice. It is advisable to resort to prayer, because when our loved ones are torn from us, despair engulfs us and we feel we shall never find anyone anywhere in whom our life's pride and joys can be combined. All the world's riches are powerless to restore the dead. It seems nothing remains but to fill our eyes with tears and spasm our throats with sobs. Our hearts break with sorrow, as we deplore our loss. All of this while our selfishness rises, so that we even reprimand God. We do not, for a moment, stop and think why we should act so. Does it help the deceased? Do not the laws of God and Nature have a right to run their course? What right has anyone to be so selfish? Should you offend the Almighty and make it unpleasant for the departed one, who would prefer you to give him more immediate help by your prayers and good deeds? Be considerate! Do not be cruel to the Lord and to your deceased loved one!

Sink not deep into sorrow, for it tends to complaints. Hold out for time, and time will heal your injury. Remember you have a soul, set to work to benefit it while you can before you have others sob for you; because your days, as well as those of all of us here, are numbered. We know not at what hour or day our eyes will close on this world of sin.

Passion of Christ, comfort us, and have mercy upon our departed loved ones; and over their graves let the Cross shed its grateful shadow, and let their souls benefit with the blessings of our Creator!

III

Mortality and conflict are essential deficiencies belonging to human nature; they cannot be rectified by tinkering with Nature. They can be supplied, for rectification, by necessary gifts from Heaven, to which human nature has no claim; they must be earned.

While living, we do not have nor can we achieve complete happiness; the goods of our bodies—health, strength, beauty, and pleasure—are delicate things, they wax and wane, and at death they disappear entirely. Our miseries and disappointments with which we rack our bodies are only in the conscious, and are of no avail to us if we do not offer them for some good in the hereafter.

The years take from us everything except our souls; we lose our vigor, mental force, our relatives and friends, and our social standing in the active world. In a dangerous, chronic illness, as well as in old age, when we see our friends and possessions going, when we see our life ebbing away, we can get an incentive to make up for a better acceptance, and for better hopes in the world ahead of us, the Goal Divine.

During life we must train ourselves to suffer patiently all of our tribulations, and offer them for the benefit of our departed relatives and friends, or for ourselves. Who is afraid of pain and misery is afraid of his own nature, because he has not developed patience within himself. We must work with our final goal always in mind, because God owes us nothing; but since He loves good and hates evil, He will punish us for our badness and reward us for our good. The better the life we can pursue, the greater benefit we will earn and may avoid the eternal punishments.

God's justice and mercy are immeasurable. No man can outdo Him. In some of our courts there may be a show of justice with mercy added, but, in general, the average enforcement officer, from high to low, is imbued with the importance of his office; and with him there is no merciful consideration, but strictly "it is the law." God does not do that: He is patient, all bearing, and all ready to forgive, if you will just show Him that you are honestly sorry.

You can express your sorrow for your sinful life, because greater sinners than yourself have done it. Why not you?

Luther, even as Voltaire, on his deathbed, realized that his end was near, and brought to mind all the sins he had committed: causing the Protestant Reformation, because the Pope could not free him from his perpetual vows to God, and liberate him to marry the Abbess with whom he had been carrying on a secret love affair; the distortion of the Bible to suit his ideas and motives; approving of polygamy and advising King Henry VIII of England to adopt it; advising men that, by belief only in Christ, they could commit adultery and murder a thousand times a day without periling their salvation; denouncing and damning the findings and the personality of Copernicus; massacring the German peasants who demanded of him some evangelical fairness; and many, many other sins which came to torment him in his last hours. He secretly sent a servant to bring him a Roman Catholic priest, so that he could make a Confession and return to the Catholic fold. But the forces of evil, the Frankenstein he helped to establish, its members around his bedside, gave him no opportunity to see the priest, because the latter was barred at the entrance door.

If such a man, who declared that reason should be destroyed in all Christians, could attempt to save his soul, why cannot you?

Our Church, which through the ages has been a patron of arts and education, has also for centuries been a patron of mercy to the Prodigal Son.

We must remember that death is not the final thing; it is merely a change from one place and one life, to another place and to another existence. The life in an apple seed cannot produce a tree, nor the blossoms and the fruit, unless the seed die in the earth. No perfect happiness can come to man unless he dies and grows into eternity.

Conclusion

IN CONCLUSION, let me advise once more, that, in believing, our emphasis must be on God, on His power and wisdom. All the mysteries, as of the origin of the universe; of life and living beings; of man and of his soul; also those of the Holy Trinity; the Immaculate Conception; the Virgin Birth of Jesus; the Resurrection of the Body and Life after Death; and of the others, must be considered from that point. If God is all-powerful, He can contemplate and perform anything, no matter how baffling it is to us. It is His affair and mostly concerns Him; we have not much to say, but to submit ourselves to Him and serve Him and meditate the mysteries.

Concerning miracles, and the miraculous powers of relics and sacramentals, we must consider that if Christ could endow His garments with powers to perform miracles, all holy relics and sacramentals we have can be endowed by Him with the same; and this includes all medals, to the metal of which we do not pray, but to what they portray; and to the symbol of something that does possess spiritual power—the blessing and prayer of the Church.

To the Greatness of God, the best we can do is stand in awe and reverence before Him and His works, His law and order in Nature and the universe.

Résumé

I

Persons become atheists, agnostics, or skeptics mostly because of wrong associations in education, at work, or in their social endeavors. Their mode of living is also responsible in many ways. Usually their ideas were adopted from other freethinkers.

An unbeliever is like a blind man who prefers to believe there are no things such as light and color which others see. He contends that there must be a constant thought, desire, or predisposition for his evolution to produce a thing, but cannot explain in what that thought existed before the first brain was formed, or where his evolution got its know-how. He cannot explain where the thought got its knowledge of acoustical, optical, and other laws, so that it could produce the organs of our senses and those of other bodily functions.

The freethinker is usually self-centered and selfish. He lives with his head in the clouds. He does not desire to believe in a God or to belong to any church.

Modern discoveries have banished the old traditional conceptions of matter and Darwinism upon which atheism was based.

A person believes in many things he does not and cannot see or visualize, but he does not want to believe in God, who reveals Himself in many various ways, because of his irrationality. As all unseen things must be revealed by research and investigation, God being unseen must be revealed by the same methods to some extent, outside of faith. Scientists are not authorities on God and religion. Their work is confined to the composition of things and of the laws that govern them; beyond that, their opinions are personal and are derived mostly from a synoptic mind.

The mind, if it tried by means of its own energy and powers, could come to know God without revelation or instruction. The

Creator of All reflects Himself in everything, but a prejudiced mind does not want to see.

God to be seen would have to be visible in a materialistic form. He would therefore be limited by space. He would not be able to permeate through the spiritual state. But being in Spirit and Godly essence, He can permeate everything and reveal Himself in all processes.

God cannot be measured or proved like a mathematical equation.

Conceiving the "idea of God" is proof of the existence of the Almighty. All of Nature is a book, on every page of which we can read of the Creator, because natural history is the history of the Works of God. Our minds reflect some of the characteristics of their origin, God. You cannot conceive of thinking and planning, which is so evident in everything about us, without a personality that does the work. In the universe, it is God, a Personal God.

Intelligence is a faculty of spiritual substances. The First Cause was a Spirit, it had intelligence, knowledge, and will power, it was a Personal God.

At the creation of the world, motion was not born of itself, there had to be an outside cause to produce it. This cause had to have intelligence to know how that motion was to be produced and for what purpose. This cause was the First Cause, God.

Our world does not exist for itself or from itself, and it could not give birth to itself. Our world and the law and order in this universe required an intelligent Cause, who was God.

Order in living organisms, where not only is union, cohesion, and combination, but also a principle of life, action, intelligence, and moral order, reveals a Master Creator, God.

Order suggests purpose. Purpose suggests a mind, and this suggests God.

The laws and order that govern the heavens amaze you with the Wisdom of God. The laws of Nature imply a lawgiver, who is no one else but God. The cosmological argument directly refutes the system of materialism.

God does not fall within the province of any natural sciences.

God is not constantly interfering with the laws and processes of Nature, but endows Nature and her laws to achieve their ends.

In the numerous acts of Providence we see the Hand of God.

Nature, which is Providence, is in turn the Art of God, by which He makes and governs everything, and which reveals all subsistence is on the Mind of God.

Nothing was produced in this universe without sufficient reason. The end would not be an end, if it were not preconceived or desired. An end supposes the choice, disposition, and direction of the means.

The wonders of the construction of man, animal, plant, and everything else in this universe, including their various parts, compositions, forms, functions, etc., cannot be attributed to the fatal, blind, atheistic evolution derived from the supposed works of primitive molecules. Whence came the gaseous state, the locale of these works, if matter is not eternal?

The Almighty created matter, knows its composition, and understands how to handle it. Producing miracles is not impossible for Him. He is the only one who has a Universal Mind and He is the only Unlimited Authority on everything. Nothing is impossible for Him unless it is a contradiction, but these do not exist, cannot exist.

The First Cause of order always precedes the physical cause of effect.

Geology reveals order existed from the beginning of the creation of matter.

Life has no weight or dimensions, but it has force. In all living processes there is some mysterious operating power; some guiding principle.

Matter, by itself, cannot think, it has to be manipulated by someone possessing intelligence, be it man or God. All instincts reveal the wonders of a Creator.

God is the reflection of power, law, and order, and the wonders in everything; He is the property that makes the material world go; He is a Spirit; the Essence of a Cosmic Consciousness that gives force and power to direct, form, drive, and make things; He is the Consciousness of the universe, being more basic than space or matter; He is the life and power of motility; He is the mystical entity that makes everything in this universe click; and He is the Creator of us all and of everything about us.

I I

The conception of an idea requires more than one fact. One fact is not knowledge. People should differentiate between theory and fact. They should never take theory for a fact. A fact is something proven and which cannot be disproven, while a theory is still in the guessing stage.

Everybody is limited by the extent of their vision and knowledge. Their capacities are all limited, they cannot trust their senses.

Behind the physical world is an unseen realm, more fundamental, which cannot be described in physical terms. Our consciousness is rooted in this unseen world, which is not built of atoms.

During the formation of the earth, life was not always possible here.

Chance, hazard, and the fatal law of necessity were all blind and dumb, they could not set or produce order, choose, will, or understand; they could not beget free beings and intelligence.

There has never been any spontaneous generation; organisms arose and arise from pre-existing organisms of the same species.

The single cell—amoeba—does not produce life within itself; it was and is endowed with life and instinct.

Primitive germs of life could not come from some other planet. There is no life upon any planets near us, and there are so many dangerous hazards to life existing in space, a cell of life coming from a far-distant point would never reach here. If there was life on a distant star, how did it commence there?

Processes of evolution can be behind the changing forms of matter, but only a Supreme Intelligence can be behind those processes.

To produce in atheistic evolution, a thought, desire, or condition would have to be constant and the least interrupted, because, as soon as a lapse occurs, the opposite forces tend to remove or retard progression. Besides these forces, much of living creation cannot reason and express itself steadily in thought or desire. Therefore there appears to be something wrong with maintaining the theory of such an evolution.

It is questionable how evolution could establish equilibrium in this world; and how did it know of all the hazards every living thing had to face; and where did it get the brains to plan and develop means of action and defense?

In our daily lives if we would apply the query of "how could evolution produce this" to the many things we encounter, our minds would be full of doubt as to the honesty of the evolutionary processes, because most of them are based on circumstantial evidence.

When a person knows how things happen, he understands; but when he lacks knowledge, he doubts or disbelieves. And when anything appears fanciful and unbelievable, he will not put his faith in it. When he adds prejudice or bias to his reasoning, he paralyzes his intellect.

Experience did not produce all of our knowledge; part of it was bestowed by God.

There are no connections between thought and the chemical elements of the brain matter. The brain does not generate thoughts or ideas, but acts only as an instrument of the thoughts or ideas, as the eye is to the soul.

You do not see with your eye, hear with your ear, taste with your tongue, and feel with your hand; they are all merely instrumental in carrying the impulses to your brain. And in this brain there your soul receives all, knows what is coming in, and how to respond to same.

The soul is created by God as matter cannot produce spirit.

The spirit is not the mind, it is the soul wherein the mind is seated.

The soul is the principle by which we live, move, and have

identity. It knows good and evil; justice and truth; and perceives the connections existing between premises and conclusions.

It is your soul which sees, hears, and talks in your dreams, and not your body organs.

The existence of the soul can be logically illustrated by many examples of things about us; for briefness, let us take the automobile: the car represents the body of man; the motor, the life of man; and the driver, the soul of man.

The soul is endowed with many faculties, most of which are not acquired but present at birth.

Emotions are not things of matter; they are attributes of the spirit.

No one has ever seen God or a soul, but neither has anyone seen an electron, the power of a chemical element, the composition of a split atom, but nevertheless believes in them, so why not put your faith in God and the existence of the soul, which are so evident? You cannot? Why, because you are stubbornly Zolaized?

The soul of man comes into existence only by the direct creative act of God; it cannot be produced by matter nor be generated by human parents.

The soul can direct its consciousness. It expresses itself through the body and can leave the body and express itself outside of it; or can use the body, while it is in a somnambulant condition, to do things, as in sleep-walking or under hypnotic suggestion.

There is a similarity between a living being and a whirlpool. The latter is of permanent form, but the water moving within it is constantly changing without disturbing its individuality, just as in the living being the constituents are constantly changing, but the form and individuality remain intact. In the whirlpool it is the unseen force that maintains the form, while in the living being it is the soul.

Life is an attribute of the soul, which the latter governs, but life cannot reason or have the attributes of the mind, which only the soul possesses.

Man's soul, alone, is capable to grasp humor so as to produce laughter.

III

Every living organism is made up of two parts, the visible and the invisible.

Man is a duality, he is composed of a visible body and an invisible soul. The soul is the "person" in the body, it is the vital principle of the body. Man is not his soul, but his body and soul, united, make him.

Man is not a delusion because he exists. His brain and body undergo constant changes, but his soul remains unchangeable and maintains his identity.

Man's cycles of existence on this earth are evolved from other cycles of existence and pass on into still other cycles. The first cycle had its origin in God, and the final end of all cycles will be, also, in God.

An impudent atheist expects a description of God when he cannot satisfactorily describe himself.

Man is the only foundation upon which any social order can be erected.

Nothing is more capable of improvement than man. Only the cynical fatalist imagines he is hopeless and cannot change.

There is no difference in the mental capacity of a man of today and one of prehistoric times. If the ancient had the opportunity to be born and raised under the living and educational conditions of today, he would resemble the modern man in intelligence and behavior. If his child was, from his birth, brought up and educated in our modern atmosphere, no one would recognize the difference between him, the child of an ancient, and a child of our times. And all this is because, from the date of man's origin, his mind was endowed with a certain complete capacity for the maintenance of thought and its use. Though modern man has accumulated much advanced thought, he has not as yet used his capacity to its fullest.

In all the operations of a human body, cells function co-operatively to produce effects as members of the whole organism, because there is life and a soul to bind and direct them. When this life and the soul leave, their functions become dead.

We have a gradation of life and spirit as: life with body without spirit—cell; life with body and with spirit—man; life with spirit and without body—angels. All of this gradation dominated by an All-Life and All-Spirit Entity—God.

God gave us music, graded with different sounds, from the low vibrations to the higher tones; He made our hearing and tasting mechanisms, with graded size and length of fibers or buds to do their proper functions; He gave us the light beam, graded into different-colored rays and each of different wave length; He gave us plants and animals graded into species, each of its own kind; and He gave us men of different types and colors. Could it not be possible He created all particular and appropriate gradations of life at one time in each geological period, and just for that period, reserving better gradations for better developed eras? And all not evolving from one kind, but each of its own kind and its own kind of species? There is so much endowment of His in things and beings of this world, why could not it be possible that each era of the world's evolution was endowed with its specific species of life?

Many of the rudimentary things found in our bodies may have been necessary during the development of an embryo or a sperm, or of something else which we may have overlooked somewhere, or at certain stages of development and carried over. Opinions and ideas were formerly built upon scientific assumption and considered as factual, but they do not exist today. In the past, many things were considered useless by science and medicine, and scientists were positive about their belief. Today some of these same things are considered of great value to man. If science can know positive and unchangeable facts, there may be more reliance on its "facts" concerning man, life, and evolution.

We have an opposite to everything in our physical world. We have forces which produce progressive changes and forces which act against them to obviate those changes.

In research a scientist has a motive, which is a mystery; he visualizes it and works to attain it. A religious person has a motive, which is a mystery; he visualizes it and works to attain it also.

God endowed man with a conscience whereby he knows good from evil, and knows what to enjoy and what to be sorry for. As there is reward for good and punishment for evil, here on earth, there will be the same when we pass to the other realm. We would not be endowed with the capacity of enjoying or suffering if there were no Heaven or Hell existing.

Man's actions have for themselves an end; be they good, the end is Heaven; be they evil, the end is Hell.

Freedom of thought is liberty to think the truth and not to think as one pleases. Free will is to act as one pleases, but within the Commandments of God and the moral law, not contrarywise.

When man's mental processes are under control of his conscious self, the soul, he does his real thinking. His unconscious self is the brain, which is a storehouse of his thoughts, upon which the mind of the soul acts when in the course of thinking.

Man is casually telepathic; God is completely and universally telepathic.

Concerning the origin of life, the spark had to be given to the chemical constituents of certain cells and they had to be endowed with properties to do their work, just as the Creator had planned. No matter how or in what way or form their progress was, there had to be an Intelligence, a First Cause, to guide and direct the creation which later culminated in man, whom God endowed with a soul and intelligence.

The temperatures and conditions had to be favorable for life to develop, because heat or cold would retard or prevent life's effort to evolve.

IV

Christ established One Church and warned everybody, in the New Testament, that others would be advanced by man and false prophets, but that His Church, being the real and genuine one, would outlast them all and withstand all efforts to destroy it.

His Church has been established on an unchangeable base; it does not get old-fashioned or need innovations. The principles on which it was founded are here today, and will be the same centuries hence.

The Pope, the head of the Church, is not infallible. He is only infallible when he speaks, ex cathedra, on matters or questions of faith or morals. The Church is not and should not be confined to the pulpit and the Scriptures, it has a right to extend its influence into every walk of life. The Church has the right to look after its sheep and their interests.

If one religion is as good as another, Christ would not have needed to come and set up His own Church.

Whatever Christ revealed, be it the Blessed Trinity or Holy Eucharist, it must be as He said, because He is God and Almighty as the Father who is in Him. If we believe His being God, but doubt the things He revealed, we sin against Him.

In the Holy Eucharist, every particle of the Host and every drop of wine truly is the whole and entire body and blood of Christ. When the bread is changed into the body of Christ, it is changed into the real body, that is, flesh and blood of the Savior, but not a body wholly of flesh. When the wine is changed into His blood, it is not dead blood; it is living and active in a living active body. When we receive the Holy Eucharist in only one form, it does not make any difference, because the whole body and blood is present in every part. And it is not a dismembered part!

We are not cannibals because we eat the Holy Eucharist, which is body and blood. Do we not eat meat, steaks, and poultry to nourish ourselves? Those are flesh and blood, are they not?

The Bible is a revelation of spiritual verities and not a textbook of natural science. While the sacred writers communicate great spiritual and religious truths, they merely reflect the views on natural science as it was prevalent in their day. The Church's primary concern is with the truths of religion, and not with those of science.

Private interpretation of the Scriptures was scorned and forbidden by the Apostles. They built a Church to do that delicate work.

The meat of the Gospels was known to the Apostles and the early Church Fathers. Whatever the Apostles wrote in epistles or instructions to their disciples or churches in their locale of teaching, was, of course, not known to every Apostle, because each one circulated in his circumscribed area. After their deaths, all their writings were collected and the New Testament was formed. The Gospels are all about the works of Christ and His sayings, and about the activities of the Apostles. They were all there, witnessed nearly everything. How could they not know the Gospels before they were written? And if any one of them forgot any part of them, the Holy Spirit had come to enlighten them.

The mentality and customs of the people of biblical days of the Old and New Testament cannot be compared with those of people of the present time. Their word meanings can be misinterpreted, unless one knows their original meanings. For example: The word "eunuch" did not mean a castrated man, but a man who lived in restraint of sex; and the words "brother" and "sister" meant cousins. This custom is still prevalent in certain European countries, where they have no word for "cousin." Only "brother" and "sister" are used.

God did not devise the Ten Commandments to regulate Himself. He gave them to man to make him live as the Creator expects him to. The Ten Commandments are a collection of general laws; they do not bind God. He could order anything contrary to them in any instance. He was the Author of them. He could suspend them in any instance wherever He found it feasible.

Many persons have warped religious concepts, according to which they set the pattern of their lives.

People attend religious services on Sundays, holy days, and on weekdays because they consider themselves sinners and want their souls to be saved. The "pseudo-saints" stay home and enjoy their earthly paradise.

Persons who attend their church must remember they are in a House of God and not in a theater. They must come to pray and have something to pray from, to keep their minds from wandering about.

In general, you must pray and have faith, because faith perfects reason, it does not contradict reason; it is concerned with knowledge that is above reason.

When you learn to pray and pray correctly, you will find that the help you ask for has been near you all the time.

God and the Church forbid idolatry, but sanction veneration of the presentations of Christ, the Virgin, and the Saints. Catholics do not pray to the images, medals, pictures, etc., but pray before them because the veneration adds value to their petitions and praying.

In honoring and venerating Holy Mary, the Mother of God Jesus, we do not take away anything from her Son, whom we worship. It is because of Him we glorify Her. Christ was not stupid as a God not to know who and what kind of a woman He wanted to be His Mother.

In the first centuries Our Lady was venerated very highly. We find in the catacombs Her picture with Child on the walls. This was a Christianity that was close to its sources.

A man and woman who unite to marry and bring forth offspring do their God-ordained duty. The child has no grounds for grievance because he was born without his consent, it is his own misfortune that God wanted him.

Parents coddle their children too much, spoiling them for the present and for the future. No youngster should be made to feel independent until he becomes of age. Parents should not give minors any spending money allowances, but where it is necessary they should have an accounting of every penny spent. In dealing with their youngsters, parents should be kind but firm.

Sin will find you out! Many sinners carry the marks of their transgressions upon their features. Sinful inclinations are revealed by thoughts, words, mode of dress, or choice of pleasure.

You strive hard to have all the luxuries of living within your immediate possession. You have to have a car, a television set, the latest model of washer and dryer; also a freezer, a boat, and probably a summer home by the ocean or river; and for all of this you strive hard, putting yourself and your family deep into debt, even robbing the Lord and His Church of their due for your selfish needs. A day may come like a bolt out of the sky, and all this passing fancy may fall through and calamity hit you so hard that you will cry to God, to the God you robbed and snubbed and insulted with your living. Will He hear and listen to you? He may, but whether he will give you any help will depend upon His justice and mercy. Why not lay aside a little of that effort of yours and strive a little for the good of your soul? Remember, sinner, everything you crave that is beyond your means is liable to be credited to the sin of gluttony.

Birth and death are miracles which no one can explain.

Death is not the end of everything; it is only a transitional period of man's existence from one world to another. It is a physical phenomenon and just another law of Nature where we lose our bodies but not our spirit, the soul.

Remember the departed so that you may be remembered someday!